Transcending Depression

Larry Dreben

Also by Larry Godwin

Surviving Our Parents' Mistakes

Transcending Depression

Quest Without a Compass

Larry Godwin, Ph.D.

Transcending Depression:
Quest Without a Compass
Larry Godwin, Ph.D.

Printed in the United States of America.

ISBN: 978-0-578-69491-7

Author's e-mail address: GodwinLarry73@Gmail.com

Font: 11 pt. Palatino

I dedicate this book to my readers.

May you find within these pages what you seek.

Depression lies. It tells you you've always felt this way, and you always will. But you haven't, and you won't.
HALLEY CORNELL

Being depressed is an opportunity to make a new beginning and to take a new direction. Once you accept the fact that for now, you're stalled and lost, then you can take the first step.
MAXIME LAGACÉ

It is only in our darkest hours that we may discover the true strength of the brilliant light within ourselves that can never, ever, be dimmed.
DOE ZANTAMATA

Sadness is but a wall between two gardens.
KAHLIL GIBRAN

For a seed to achieve its greatest expression, it must come completely undone. The shell cracks, its insides come out, and everything changes. To someone who doesn't understand growth, it would look like complete destruction.
CYNTHIA OCCELLI

Contents

Preface   xiii

Acknowledgements   xv

Foreword   xvii

Introduction   xix

1 1971-1980   1

2 1981-1990   17

3 1991-2000   43

4 2001-2010   79

5 2011-2019   103

Afterword   125

Appendix I: Psychiatric Medications the Author Has
        Taken   129

Appendix II: Depression Survival Guide   131

Appendix III: Chess in the Labyrinth   139

Preface

The primary motivation for presenting my history is to encourage others who grapple with either chronic depression or occasional bouts. I hope my journey resonates with some, validates feelings, and sparks the thoughts *I'm not alone* and *I will feel better*.

This book can also help family members and friends of the mentally ill find compassion and enable them to understand the struggle. It could, as well, benefit those who care for the depressed, and interest the curious and the voyeur. My goal is to save lives.

xv

Acknowledgments

First, I want to thank my editor-wife, Cathy, for her unending support as I conducted my quest for better mental health. I so appreciate her encouragement of my writing this book, and am grateful she read every word and offered helpful suggestions.

I feel indebted to the members of my critique group, the Menagerie, for constructive criticism and recommendations at all phases of my writing. These individuals provided invaluable counsel that propelled me forward: Zan Bockes, Rose Dixon, Jenny Greil, Samantha Steven, and Robert Winslow.

I also want to acknowledge the helpful critique the members of the Missoula Public Library MakerSpace creative writing workshop provided. I value comments these members made: Eryn Aston, Anna Chithelen, Kare Enga, Daniella Garvue, Robin Kolb, Owen Kuhn, Nora Moseman, Maureen Palmersheim, and especially those of the leader, Rachael Parkin.

Foreword

Larry's book contains compelling insights with the potential to help others. It concretely shows what depression is like, which might aid someone experiencing it for the first time, or someone unfamiliar with it, to understand it. A person cannot just take a pill to fix the ailment and cannot simply snap out of it. There's no single cause and no universal cure. Other depressed people can relate to Larry's contradictory thoughts and ambivalence, and his memoir can engender compassion in the loved ones of those living with despondency.

Besides offering observations on his illness and how he coped with it, the book weaves Larry's story, a brave one that draws in the reader, with his clinical analysis of the results of the medications he took. That story furnishes markers that move the narrative along. What went on day to day greatly impacted his moods and provides context for his depression. Personal details make his writing authentic. In colorful language, he illustrates how every aspect of life, including work, love, and the pursuit of outside interests, is not just affected, but dominated, by one's mental health. The work carries a man's voice but women can identify with the content as well.

From time to time, Larry incorporates humorous notes that counter the heavy tenor of many of his journal entries. Flickers of delight crop up to round out his character, and occasional quiet victories add positivity. The disclosure of his ups and down makes the account understandable and accessible.

The book constitutes a study of Larry's depression, as revealed in his journal, rather than simply a collection of entries. In part the tone suggests a technical treatise, but emotional events intervene, jolting the reader. The style comprises a blend of the expository, the poignant, and the quasi-scientific.

Transcending Depression combines an objective outlook with subjective introspection. Seldom does Larry stray into exaggeration or self-dramatization. His search for rationality is the book's main theme. In the end, his message is uplifting without being overly dramatic or sentimental.

Concise entries capture the feeling of riding on a roller coaster with interspersed periods of numbness; they pack a punch. Larry walks a tightrope and, in response to medications and external events, reacts like a yo-yo. He spins his wheels, painfully trying to make himself a better person, trying to learn from his mistakes. He continually seeks balance.

The book exhibits a driving desire to know, to figure things out, and to improve rather than give up. In reality, this process applies to everyone who yearns to achieve personal growth. One of us found his quest both harrowing and awe-inspiring. The members of our group found much to relate to; one person found all Larry's potential readers inside herself. Others, of whom only one suffers from depression, said the book resonates with them and speaks to them personally.

Larry's book provides an unguarded window into his experience, with refreshing, brutal honesty and sincerity. It demonstrates strength of character and arouses empathy. The reader is invested in Larry throughout and wants him to succeed.

Members of the Menagerie Critique Group

Introduction

In 1971, at age 29, I recognized I suffered from depression. This personal narrative represents the chronology of my illness, the highs and lows, as well as my attempts to understand it and cope with it. Selected entries from my personal journals over a span of 49 years constitute the source and follow an authentic progression over time. In them, I relate insights about the origins of my disorder. I also describe thoughts and feelings that arose and my reactions to events that took place at various times, as influenced, for better or worse, by psychiatric medications and supplements.

I chose to include in this book perhaps one-tenth of one percent of all the entries in the dozens of journals I wrote. Some years contain few items, often because my moods were generally high, but, especially in later years, to avoid repetition. I do not wish to bore or overwhelm the reader by recounting again earlier realizations about issues that caused depression, or by duplicating conclusions I'd previously arrived at but later forgotten. For the same reason, I also omitted some thoughts about subsequent experiments with the same medications and supplements that yielded similar results as before, as well as some passages about trials with new ones that, like so many others, led to dead ends.

I edited most in-the-moment thoughts to make the narrative flow more smoothly while retaining the substance. I also substituted "my friend," "my therapist," and "my doctor" for proper names of persons who do not recur later in the story.

In the afterword, I present overall observations about my quest and sum up. In the process, I identify recurring themes and point out strategies that have enabled me to survive.

I hasten to point out this book comprises a case study of one. The causes and symptoms of my depression will not correspond with those of every individual, for each of us is unique. It would not be appropriate to assume I epitomize the depressed person.

Chapter 1
1971-1980

1971

Englewood, Colorado

This weekend my new friends in Crested Butte exposed me to ideas that should make my life easier and keep me from getting depressed as easily or often. The first is I must love myself before I can love others or find inner contentment. Second: Others cannot hurt me; I can only allow myself to feel hurt. Third: I cannot change other people, such as inconsiderate smokers, only my reactions to them. So when I get dispirited, the questions arise, why have I let myself become hurt? And why have I stopped loving myself?

After writing up my memories of the weekend, I no longer pity myself. I no longer have to react to other people the way they appear to expect. I'll be *me*. For the first time in ages, I don't have any problems, and, for the first time ever, I feel like a man.

* * *

Expectations unfulfilled are the major source of my depression. The best thing to do is have none. If I must have them, I'll expect the worst and be prepared for the consequences.

Denver, Colorado

Today I left [my wife] Barbara, [our children] Andrea, and David and moved into a rooming house at 931 E. 17th Street. I can't stand the put-downs and domination any longer, the ways she expects me to behave, and the responsibilities she puts on me.

* * *

This summer grants my last taste of freedom for a while. I have no responsibilities except to myself: consider marital options, break isolation and meet others, journal, and accomplish personal growth. Each afternoon, barefoot, I take up residency in Cheesman Park to make new friends. After I move to Boulder in September, studying for my doctorate and teaching two accounting classes won't allow time for such luxuries.

Boulder, Colorado

I feel lonely and anxious about my future. I'm starved for love. What if my new woman friend doesn't like the frightened me? Our Friday date is only three days away.

* * *

This time we didn't click and my new friend doesn't want to see me again. I'm thinking of killing myself. But it might be a tragic mistake. I might regret it later.

* * *

Yesterday at the Colorado-Wyoming football game, the thought occurred to me, in the last analysis, only I can bring myself out of this misery. No one else can help significantly when I'm as depressed as I was Saturday morning. At times like that, I should not think in terms of "What can someone do for me?" but, rather, "What can I do for myself?"

How did I pull out of it? I planned my evening: fix chili dogs, play my new Moody Blues album, perhaps study a bit, and listen to my radio. It felt good knowing I could do it alone and dig it. Then the phone rang, my neighbor came to the door, I met her sister, and it was beautiful.

* * *

A week ago was Super Saturday. My girlfriend stayed the night before; I met Janet at the Packer Grill in the afternoon; and that evening, I drove another woman friend to Estes Park, both of us singing to the radio. Last night Janet and I made love and she spent the night for the first time. Do I deserve to be this happy?

* * *

Barbara and I should have split long ago. I married Mother's twin, living to please her, watching myself constantly. She delighted in controlling me, and disapproved of my weight, my hair, the way I act in social situations, even the way I yawn! She demanded submission. But still, despite her hostility, living with her felt secure until she started fucking other men.

* * *

Janet has moved in with me and my world seems complete. She even accepts my need for alone time.

1972

After nine years of marriage, I'm free. Today our divorce became final. What a shame it happened on Leap Year Day – I
can celebrate it only every four years.

* * *

I'm jealous of Janet's friendships with other men and it irks me
she keeps a private journal. What's she writing about me? I'm
anxious because we have no commitments. It bothers me I'm
so insecure and depend on her this much. I feel inadequate,
just like last spring before Crested Butte. I've made no progress since December and am setting myself up for deep depression.

* * *

If I can't let Janet go, I'll lose her. I must become self-reliant. I
can't depend on her, only on myself.

1973

How often I write in this journal is an index of how much personal growth concerns me. I haven't written much lately.

1974

One important thing I learned this week is when sad and unhappy, I should go off alone and work it out myself instead of
depressing everyone around me.

Corvallis, Oregon

These days I have no happy times or sad times, either. My life is even and measured with no peaks or valleys. I feel content but wonder if I'm alive.

* * *

Janet and I are settling into our duplex and I'm getting ready to teach my first classes at Oregon State. I feel excited about this new life chapter but anxious I don't have enough time to fully prepare. I've never taught seniors and grad students before.

1975

Sometimes when I've been despondent for several days, it helps to discipline myself by saying, "I'm going to think only positive thoughts." Enough is enough!

* * *

Tonight Janet and I exchanged karma. When she picked me up at the university, I was bouncy and gay but she was irritable. As time passed, her spirits rose and I became pensive and serious.

* * *

At those times when I'm weak, needy, and depressed, I must remember there's someone who feels worse. To that person, I would appear whole.

1976

I gave up Janet today. She moved out and took all her possessions. If she wants to be solitary to "get herself together," it
will be just that: without my support. We had no commitments.

I will make it alone. But I just wrote her that although angry, I
want her to come back to me. At this time I can accept these
contradictory thoughts and will try to be patient.

After dreaming about it for years, now I have the freedom to
pursue other women but no longer the desire.

* * *

Although I'm lonely, several parts of living alone have great
appeal. Like getting up in the morning when I want, exercising
by myself, and listening to music when and as loud as I wish. I
can put on the aftershave Janet hated. I haven't yet learned to
live with myself so I'm not ready to live with someone else
again.

* * *

A major difference between separating from Barbara and from
Janet is that after leaving my wife, I wasn't used to smiles and
affection. Wow, do I miss Janet.

* * *

Last night a woman friend didn't give me what I wanted (a
good screw) but she gave me what I needed (good advice).

* * *

How am I today? Teetering on the cusp between depression and euphoria.

* * *

I want someone to take care of me. In my 34 years I have never accepted full responsibility for my own welfare, feelings, or happiness – a dangerous state. What would it feel like to not give women power over me? I've never approached that ideal; it's totally alien.

1977

While Janet lived with me and for months afterward, I was a half. I'm aiming to become a whole. Right now I'm at least a three-quarters.

* * *

What took me out of my melancholy yesterday was talking with people, not spending time alone. It was very good chatting with several friends, then sleeping by myself.

1978

After four months of dating, Carol and I have broken up. I ended the relationship, mainly because she read my journal while I was taking a shower. Then she blasted me for what I'd written about us: doubts I'd ever want to live with her. But I deeply miss our closeness. For now I'm going to have to reconcile myself to having no lover.

* * *

For the third straight day, I'm feeling totally apathetic about everything. It was a chore getting prep done for tomorrow's classes. I did the bare minimum. It's impossible to give – other people just aren't worth my time.

* * *

Last night on the phone I told Carol I was hurting. At the end of the conversation, she said, "Well, I leave you to your depression."

* * *

I want Carol back and tonight have no motivation to live without her. That's really sick.

It's distressing there's nothing between living and dying. The life switch is either on or off. I want to stop this pain but lack the courage to kill myself. Death is so final.

I could shoot Carol, then myself.

* * *

The fact I'm desperate is tremendously liberating. I contemplate doing things my filtering system would ordinarily censor, like moving back to Colorado this summer.

* * *

Perhaps I should listen to more cheerful music. Linda Ron-
stadt's songs are incredibly depressing. I should play more of
John Denver's.

* * *

Over coffee at the Beanery this morning, I searched for someone to save me. I decided to save myself and left.

* * *

Phone conversations with Mother bring me down because
she's always unhappy. Tonight I told her that each time we
talk, I'd like her to tell me one positive thing.

* * *

I don't want to teach any longer. I'm sick of the deadlines and
pressure, sick of the endless interruptions, sick of answering
the same questions, sick of advising and serving on commit-
tees, SICK. Just because I'm good at something doesn't mean I
have to stick with it.

I'm derailing myself from the tenure track but will honor my
commitment to finish this school year. Now I feel freer to be
myself in the classroom, to stop screening my words. I'm no
longer as concerned about whether my students like me.

* * *

Since quitting my job, I possess more opportunity than ever
before in my life. My decision about where to live doesn't have
to be influenced by Mother, my job, or my woman. Only me! I

could move somewhere the sun shines in the winter. I can change my name.

1979

At least when I'm depressed, I'm in the now. In fact, all my feelings are in the now. Only thoughts can exist in the past or future.

* * *

Most times when despondency comes, there's a spark of strength I can choose to act from and still be me. With other people, I do often have choices, a set of alternative responses, some more tactful than others, that are genuine yet fit my mood.

* * *

No event is depressing. I may feel depressed; if so, I take responsibility.

* * *

When I'm feeling morose and relief finally comes, it happens because I discover a plan. One that should keep me centered on a healthy track for a while. The interesting thing is, there's no consistency to the type of plan. I believe it's the spontaneous formation of the plan that's critical, that provides the incentive and energy to emerge from my gloom. The shape or content is irrelevant.

Durango, Colorado

Dejection overcomes me when I'm dishonest with someone. Last night I fought hard to hold back my anger at my closest friend here for trying to shame me for drinking wine. I acknowledged the feeling but it didn't die. It's still here this morning, plus now I'm down on myself for not being truthful.

* * *

Many times I can readily talk myself out of the dumps. It's clear I don't always want to.

* * *

Today I'm mildly dejected but have no idea why. Everything's going great in my life – I don't have a thing to complain about. Yet nothing appeals to me, not even listening to music. Could it be hormonal, this depression? I certainly don't feel like being around anyone. I'm most content sitting in my favorite chair, quite alone.

* * *

[My ten-year-old son] David is visiting from Boulder. Yesterday we took a fun picnic lunch up to the Gold King Mill. But today I can't stand the sight of him. After just having [my twelve-year-old Daughter] Andrea here for five days before he came, I desperately need my own space. I'd like to find a hole, crawl down it, and cry myself to sleep.

* * *

When I can't get in touch with anything besides the blues, maybe I'm just not aware of what's going on in my life that causes them.

1980

Low spirits engulfed me yesterday. Unlike last fall, I decided to do something about it. Here I am on this wonderful train – it's my hospital. I'm recuperating and thinking clearly. How delightful, this Chicago adventure that depends on no one. Traveling alone, I can be totally selfish.

* * *

Since moving to Durango, I've met lots of people, made many acquaintances, but can count only one friend. I left Corvallis for what? To hike every day, usually by myself, in my favorite spot on earth until winter sets in. I abandoned my home, my support group, and a university professorship – three deaths – to live where I was sure to find a new partner. No such luck. Yes, teaching had burned me out, but the job provided purpose, self-fulfillment, social contacts, and prestige. I'm despondent and lonely, plus I crave structure.

* * *

At times I miss teaching so much, tears fill my eyes. Starting in two weeks, I'm going to teach a beginning accounting class for adults Thursday evenings at the high school. This job will give my life a framework, and enable me to help other people and pursue quality in an area where I have expertise. Although my savings are dwindling and I welcome the income, it's ironic someone should pay me.

* * *

In March I'm driving to California to take a short break from this miserable Durango winter and attend a sensory evaluation wine class at U.C.-Davis. It will also give me a chance to visit my favorite wineries. I haven't been this excited in months.

* * *

Today I tasted at Chateau Montelena, where Catherine Anne Marshall guided my tour. I dared ask her out to dinner and she accepted! Afterward she invited me to her apartment and we spent the night talking. We even discussed marriage! My mind races ahead, hoping to persuade her to visit me in Durango this spring.

* * *

It's been a month since we met. Three weeks ago, Cathy made it clear she will not be ready to live with me or any other man for at least a year and wants more experience with men. But now she says she's thinking she'll quit her job and move here. What if she doesn't? Just like after Carol left, I feel desperate. I've made her my anchor.

* * *

Being giddy and witty with a woman friend last night didn't negate my underlying sadness. Laughter on one level doesn't preclude simultaneous depression on another. Sadness and happiness are not opposite ends of a scale.

* * *

Cathy now shares my little home and, as much as her company excites and invigorates me, it's tough making the transition from single to couple after living on my own for two years. Since neither of us has a job, we spend almost all our time together. I miss my own space and feel disheartened. Today I went to see my physician and started taking antidepression pills.

* * *

Tofranil[1] is probably going to make a tremendous difference in my life. I've needed help long before this. Suicidal thoughts consumed me four summers ago when Janet left and again after moving here. I've always thought I could pull myself through anything and that positive thinking would be my salvation. But it was a losing battle, perhaps because of a chemical imbalance over which I had no control.

* * *

Cathy and I spent a wonderful summer here but both of us dread winter's coming. We've decided to move to somewhere in northern California, hoping to find jobs in the wine industry. I cringe to think of packing and moving, and am anxious about finding another comfortable place to live and meaningful work. But Cathy will bolster me through this passage.

---

[1] A tricyclic antidepressant (TCA), one of the earliest the FDA approved, in 1959. See
https://www.accessdata.fda.gov/scripts/cder/daf/index.cfm?event=o verview.process&ApplNo=011838

Amarillo, Texas

I've been here two and a half weeks, hoping Mother will be able to leave intensive care and go home. Today, against her wishes, the doctor put a tube down her throat and said her chances are 30%. She blames me for not honoring her wish to die in peace. Thank God Cathy is here to help, but I need a break from her constant company – I can't think. This damned Norpramin[2] causes milder side effects than Tofranil but it isn't working.

* * *

Mother passed away at 1:30 yesterday morning. I do not feel sad. Cathy and I drove to the hospital to say our farewells. Then I notified relatives and made funeral arrangements. Everyone is pulling my strings. I'm having a hard time dealing with this pressure and wish the world would stop spinning to let me jump off for a few days. Mostly I want to get back to Santa Rosa [California] and move on with my life, but I'm the executor of Mother's will and have to make Amarillo my home base for several more weeks.

* * *

I dropped back on Norpramin from 150 to 100 mg because of trouble thinking and little sexual desire. Its benefits are questionable anyway – I feel lost and look forward to nothing. An-

---

[2] Another tricyclic antidepressant (TCA). The FDA approved it in 1964. See https://www.accessdata.fda.gov/scripts/cder/daf/index.cfm?event=B asicSearch.process

ger and dark thoughts surround me. After returning home, I
need to find a psychiatrist fast.

Santa Rosa, California

I just made a list of activities the past year that helped me overcome despondency: hiking, reading, writing, and listening to
music. Interesting, almost all involved no one else. That seems
significant. Since Cathy came to live with me, I'm often rude to
her, longing to be alone. A lack of solo time may not have
caused this depression but I require it to feel good again.

* * *

I've backed off Norpramin to 50 mg and my mood has greatly
improved! To her delight, I ravaged Cathy today.

Chapter 2
1981-1990

1981

Just like after moving to Durango, I'm vegetating and nothing brings me pleasure. I mope around our duplex, aching to apply myself again. My executor tasks are almost finished so I'm checking out part-time teaching and winery jobs around here.

In my final year teaching at Oregon State, sometimes I felt moody and apathetic, but my classes carried me through. Hence the value of regular, productive, absorbing work. I was too busy to feel melancholy.

* * *

I feel like a flower bud awaiting spring to blossom.

* * *

When I'm unhappy and can point to the cause, my despondency seems situational. When I'm sad for no apparent reason, it must be hormonal.

* * *

I seem to have a predisposition toward depression, inherited or learned from Mother. It's particularly acute when something is missing. Right now it's the lack of a central life purpose. Like enduring the long summers off in Corvallis, I can't cope with all this free time and the absence of challenge and structure. Filling in at the tasting room at Alexander Valley Vineyards last Saturday brought my spirits up enormously but it was a one-time opportunity.

* * *

My outlook needs to be positive before I can profit from alone time. When I feel dispirited, solitude takes me lower. During the school year at Oregon State, I prized seclusion because it was scarce.

* * *

If I could reach a point where my mental state was under control, I could write a hell of a good book on coping with depression.

* * *

I selected a chapter in my life, 1971-1972, just after separating from Barbara, that glistened with fondest memories. But in the midst of that period, as I basked in newfound freedom and self-discovery, I spotted evidence of deep depression.

* * *

I'm excited about the near certainty of teaching an accounting class this fall at Sonoma State. And I look forward to setting up an accounting system at Dry Creek Vineyard! They might hire me to work in the tasting room, too.

* * *

I feel like part of a family at Dry Creek. I've never before had the experience of working with people I really like and could potentially love. The four women are sensitive and affectionate – I'm so lucky to be around them almost every day. Tuesday

Linda told me I seem really happy and that she'd had with-
drawals from not seeing me since Friday. I haven't told her
about Cathy.

* * *

I'm too sensitive and overreact to everything. Today at the
winery I hope Jan will compliment me on my poem. I have an
obsession with being liked, and reveal way too much about my
tender areas to people I don't know well. Out of the blue, today I blurted out to Linda that I love her. Why do I make myself vulnerable? My moods rest totally in other peoples' hands.

* * *

My therapist says low self-esteem and depression go together.
The roots of my problem go back to when I was a child: Father
had left, Mother criticized me endlessly, and in grade school,
the other kids made fun of me and called me a sissy. How can
I foster positive feelings about myself?

* * *

I've started affirming, "I am a valuable person and deserve to
feel good about myself." And yesterday [on vacation] I set a
demanding goal and accomplished it: hiking five miles up
Cunningham Gulch over steep terrain to the Continental Di-
vide near Silverton [Colorado].

* * *

This hopelessness used to appear like a dark cloud over my
head, following me everywhere. Now it's more like a fog that

absorbs me, obscuring my clarity of vision, hearing, and thinking. It immobilizes me, makes me sluggish, and blocks memory. Is the lithium I'm taking causing this?

* * *

My job has lost its allure. Pouring wines for visitors used to be fun but it's become repetitive and boring, devoid of creativity. Besides, the owner made it clear I have no future at the winery and that rude, lazy Jan runs the tasting room. On top of that, Linda has become aloof since I told her I have a partner. So I quit.

I'm going to start my own business as a wine critic, thanks to the inheritance from Mother, and publish a monthly newsletter providing tasting notes on newly released bottlings. My expertise comes from years of experience appraising the wines I drink plus taking several classes and reading books on sensory evaluation. I need a change to shake up my life and raise my self-esteem.

* * *

My depression is cyclical. When feeling down, I must remember each episode has a beginning, middle, and end.

1982

My inability to accept the world around me deepens my depression. I'd feel less upset if I reconciled myself to the reality that drivers tailgate and throw trash from their vehicles, that smokers toss their cigarette butts on the sidewalk, and that my waitress left my cooked order out five minutes so it was cold by the time it reached my table. It does not help much to vent my anger. True, I can't change other people, but neither can I ignore their behaviors.

* * *

Publishing [my wine newsletter] *Just Released* is good for me. It offers a means of self-expression and communication with a constituency. And I'm autonomous; no one supervises me. I set my own policies and standards.

* * *

I seem to operate in a slightly different reality from other people but, fortunately, I observe the ground rules. The gap isn't too wide right now – I can choose to function normally. I like it when my reality significantly overlaps theirs because that's when differences don't matter and closeness can develop. Much of the time, Cathy's reality coincides with mine.

* * *

Today Cathy opened her catering business in Calistoga, Radish Rose, which the inheritance Mother left me made possible. Both of us are excited and optimistic.

* * *

Anger underlies many of my depressive episodes. If not at the forefront, it's always just beneath the surface, ready to leap at the slightest provocation.

Now I get it. Although Mother died two years ago, I still displace the rage I feel toward her on everyone, especially Cathy. Mother had wanted a daughter, so she curled my hair and made me wear a girl's bathing cap. I can't remember a time she hugged me or said she was proud of me. She confined me to the house most of the time I wasn't at school and burdened me with the responsibility of making her happy. She said I wasn't aggressive enough and commissioned me to fight her battles. After I became an adult, she disapproved of my clothing, my hair, my choice of friends, my profession, my home, my cooking, and my hobbies. No wonder I haven't grieved over her death. How can I resolve this childhood issue and vanquish the accumulated anger?

* * *

I don't want to acknowledge this depression as mine, that it's part of me. I refuse to claim it. It's the enemy and I must fight it because otherwise I'll succumb to it.

* * *

To wed or not to wed – that is the question. Last night, sliding into bed, I thought, *Thank God I'm a single man.*

Both Cathy and I are resisting making plans for the ceremony. Why exactly are we getting married? Just to file a joint tax return? For me, it would constitute a huge loss of freedom.

* * *

My last dinner out alone as a free man and that's OK. I'll never find another woman who loves me as much as Cathy does.

* * *

My despondency hasn't gotten better. A friend told me about a new antidepressant, Desyrel, that raises serotonin levels.

* * *

Dr. Apostle prescribed Desyrel a week ago, and since then I've felt more calm and less sad. Probably it's a placebo effect but how can I help but hope?

1983

Since starting Desyrel six weeks ago, I've felt spacey in the morning and irritable at times but, overall, peaceful and re-laxed. I'm more patient with Cathy, don't snap at her, and we make love more often. I no longer get upset at other drivers. I laugh more. I feel more energetic and my handwriting is bolder. I can't quite believe I'm the same person as last year.

* * *

Tonight I feel in harmony with the universe.

* * *

My current malaise relates to my business. I'm burned out with the repetitive nature of my work, as well as the tension and conflict, since some winery personnel dispute what I write about their products. Do I have what it takes to be a critic?

A year ago, tasting wines was a treat; now it's drudgery. Besides, if I hadn't started my publication, the $8,236 I lost in 1982 would have bought sixty cases of wine!

* * *

Depression returned, so last Friday I upped my Desyrel dose from 250 to 300 mg and have felt better. I notice flowers, enjoy music, and my singing voice is deeper.

Dr. Apostle says some people need different medication levels at different times, and my prolonged initial response was so amazing, he could not ascribe it to placebo.

* * *

In this time without depression, I can visualize the joy of having a child with Cathy.

* * *

These days my work invigorates me. I fancy myself the Ralph Nader of the wine industry, a talent scout combing the countryside for bargains and rip-offs.

* * *

Today I'm down but can laugh about it. I started with lots of energy and plans, but now feel lazy and want to be alone. No problem. Yes, I feel despondent, but also content.

* * *

Beginning in December 1982, Desyrel was my darling. For the first two months, just 200 mg worked well, but since then I've needed to gradually increase it. These last eight weeks, 400 mg kept my moods positive, but now I seem little better than before starting the drug.

[The manufacturer] Mead-Johnson told Dr. Apostle a number of patients on Desyrel develop "patient tolerance," which leads to loss of effectiveness. For the time being I'll stay on this dose but may go off it entirely, then begin again.

1984

I was going to try Nardyl but decided not to after Dr. Apostle warned me of the daunting side effects. He doesn't know of any other promising antidepressants on the market.

* * *

I feel like leaving Cathy because she appreciates me so little. She focuses all her attention on Radish Rose, which, with its schedules, controls my life as well as hers.

* * *

I raised Desyrel to 450 mg. Now I feel doped-up and exhausted, yet am still sad and apathetic. So, I'll withdraw and start over.

* * *

As a result of abstaining from Desyrel for a month, I felt energetic but depressed. So I restarted with just 150 mg and felt

great for three weeks. But eventually the drug again reached
its effectiveness limit, so once more I went off it. Now I've re-
sumed dosing and sailed right through 150 mg with no relief.
What a crappy excuse for an antidepressant but it's all I have.

1985

The past few days I haven't thought about suicide. On some
plane at least, I've resigned myself to live with this depression.
Last week it didn't seem manageable but now it does.

* * *

I have poor relations with the owners or winemakers at perhaps five percent of the wineries I visit. That's not bad. Why
not accept it and glow in the positive relationships I enjoy with
the other ninety-five?

At our therapy session yesterday, Marsha reminded me that as
a critic, I'm bound to make enemies. It goes with the territory.

* * *

I'm not at all despondent tonight. It's funny, I have a hard time
remembering how depression feels.

* * *

I was quite gloomy yesterday morning, then at noon ran a mile
and a quarter. Immediately I felt better and by evening, better
still. The effect was dramatic.

* * *

Dr. Apostle prescribed a new drug, Pamelor, to replace Desy-rel. For a month I put up with drowsiness, fatigue, difficulty urinating, decreased sex drive, dry mouth, constipation, and weight gain. And I was depressed more than half the time. Then came a week of nonstop misery.

I went off it and two days of bliss followed. But negative thoughts swamp me again so I'm going back to Desyrel.

* * *

This is my third day on just 100 mg of Desyrel and I'm basking in sunlight. I've never before gotten relief on such a low dose.

* * *

Predictably, after a few weeks, Desyrel petered out again. So I withdrew once more and now wake every morning brimming with energy. But I feel deeply depressed. Damn.

* * *

It just struck me, I have an incurable illness. I've consulted many family doctors and two psychiatrists and none possess the knowledge to heal me.

* * *

The Xanax[3] I've taken for anxiety along with Desyrel for three weeks has made me angry most of the time. Today I seriously contemplated killing myself. I took my Sominex and mini-

---

[3] Benzodiazepine medication in the same class as Valium.

cassette recorder to my office and prepared a list of instructions for Cathy. It's the closest I've come.

* * *

Now I'm doing quite well on 200 mg Desyrel and just 2-1/2 mg Xanax. But I'm going to cut back on Xanax to 1 mg morning and night and may go off it altogether.

* * *

I'm at loose ends about life, about Cathy, and about having no friends to talk to about my worries. I feel very rational when considering suicide. My work is all that holds my life together: its regimen and structure. I need to get the November issue out.

* * *

When making my monthly rounds, I admire almost every winemaker's concern for excellence. It's not love I feel, but there's a degree of concern that goes well beyond the requirement for a business interaction.

* * *

This past week with Cathy gone to visit her parents has taught me how much I need her. No one else understands and accepts me like she does. After feeling hopeless all day, when I finish my tasting appointments, I have her laughter to look forward to in the evening.

I need to talk to her more. I keep most of me to myself. I need to tell her that sometimes I want her to be light and cheery around me and other times to just hold me and listen.

1986

I can't imagine how life could be fuller. Cathy and I are close; I love my work and feel competent doing it. Best of all, I'm completely free of depression and rejoice at my inner peace, harmony, and happiness. Is the B-complex supplement the reason? More likely it's the Desyrel I started taking again. But this mood feels fragile – I don't expect it to last.

* * *

For months I've felt dispirited after eating desserts. And within fifteen minutes, sipping a sweet wine on an empty stomach at the wineries leaves me irritable and makes me want to cry.

But this I know: glucose doesn't bother me. I drank 100 grams twice in tolerance tests and had no ill effects.

* * *

My work seems trivial. I provide information to help the wealthy spend their money. I don't help ordinary people better their lives, like while teaching accounting. Maybe I'm promoting alcoholism, too.

But on the plus side, I reward quality by publishing favorable reviews for winemakers who craft exceptional products. And

to a lesser extent, I help consumers in all economic classes de-
rive more pleasure from life.

* * *

Since mailing my September issue, I seem to have figured out
what caused my severe reaction to sugar: the calcium and
multi-mineral supplements I took for months. That's a relief!
I've started drinking sixteen ounces of milk a day instead to
ease low-back pain.

* * *

I've got the post-depression blues. My old funks were so reli-
able – I could count on them, wallow in them, and use them as
excuses. As strange as it sounds, I miss my crutch.

* * *

I can no longer blame my anxiety, loneliness, and alienation on
mental illness. How frightening. I must take responsibility for
my thoughts and acts, which shape ninety percent of my life.

* * *

I'm letting my job make me fretful and despondent. The work
is frustrating, repetitious, tedious, and draining. I spend half
my life in the car, driving fifty to 150 miles a day from one
winery to the next and back home, five days a week. I walk a
fucking treadmill that never stops, even for sickness, with only
a few days off between issues. At least teaching accounting, I
had summers free.

Although believing in my work most of the time, I've lost money five consecutive years. Fortunately, Mother's bequest has been able to support our lifestyle. But now maybe it's time to quit. I bet I could sell my business for a profit.

* * *

At today's therapy session, Marsha pointed out I learned from Mother my reactions to stressful situations, like the daily ones connected to publishing *Just Released*. When the slightest thing went wrong, Mom threw up her hands or blew up. I need to become my own man and stop constantly looking for her over my shoulder.

* * *

I squandered our trip to Mexico between publishing issues. What I wanted to do was swim and lie on the beach. In those nine days, we went swimming twice! Instead, we rented a car and endured an excruciating trek over poorly marked and maintained "highways." This was my most stressful vacation ever when I just needed to relax.

1987

While I was tasting at wineries in San Luis Obispo, Cathy entertained her real estate agent for Radish Rose, which she's trying to sell, at our home during what she described as a candle-light dinner. I feel betrayed. She told me beforehand he was coming but implied the relationship was platonic. Now she says although they kissed, they didn't make love. Can I believe her? When I asked if she loves him, she said, "I don't know that I do."

Although deeply hurt, I see the situation from her point of view. Weeks ago she said she felt neglected, not just because of my long hours at work but because I made time to see three women friends for lunch or dinner and took several hikes alone. Why didn't I pay attention?

It's ironic. A few months ago I coerced her into giving up Radish Rose because *I* felt neglected. No wonder she's resentful and angry.

* * *

Tonight my life has little meaning. I feel suicidal like in Durango in 1979 before we met and in May 1980 before Cathy came to live with me. Actually, I don't want to live and I don't want to die. If only there were a way to suspend life awhile.

* * *

I've moved out. I miss Cathy but don't want to see her. And I obsess about having a sexual relationship with Linda at Dry Creek, mostly for revenge.

At first, righteous anger and self-pity bolstered me, but the last several days I've felt scared and vulnerable. The bottom has dropped out of my sense of security. It's as if Cathy died.

* * *

After a week, I've moved back but Cathy doesn't seem glad. It's like I'm on probation. Our marriage has suffered a deep wound and it will take time to heal – Marsha thinks four to six weeks.

A man friend says some of the best marriages have been saved by affairs.

* * *

I can't take the pressure to schedule my tastings any longer and have decided to sell *Just Released* to the publisher of the *International Wine Review*. The June issue will be my last. He made me a generous offer and this year I'll finally make a profit. Next week I'm going to send a farewell letter to my subscribers, explaining the transition to their new publication. I'm sad this five-year endeavor, which seemed so promising, is ending and believe eventually I'll miss some of my routines.

* * *

A few days ago, Santa Rosa Junior College offered me a section of a bookkeeping class in Petaluma this fall, and of course I accepted. I'll be happily busy teaching again and also plan to take two computer classes. Lots of structure but not too confining.

* * *

I've been enjoying Cathy's company a lot the past few days. We've had fun and made love often.

* * *

Again I've gone off Desyrel. Taking antidepressants is depressing because they slow down my mind and body and cause weight gain. I'm glad to be off them for a while and will experiment taking the amino acid supplements tyrosine and tryptophan.

1988

The amino acids didn't help and I've taken Prozac for 34 days. At best, relief has been spotty. My mood was satisfactory the entire day only four times. Side effects include exhaustion, loss of sexual desire, and cloudy thinking. I won't take a pill to-night.

* * *

This hopelessness is so strange. It's almost as if I give myself permission to feel OK when I realize an activity could be en-joyable or decide a certain dose of a certain drug will work.

* * *

What purpose does this despondency serve? I play the victim. It creates a convenient excuse when I don't want to deal with someone or undertake something unpleasant. I'm quick to point out depression runs in my family and use it as a crutch to get my way, as well as sympathy from Cathy and others. In my therapy group this week, when I confessed to suicidal thoughts, a lot of attention, warmth, and affection came to me.

* * *

My oldest brother had schizophrenia and committed suicide. My other older brother has no psychiatric problems I know of. True, Mother suffered from occasional melancholy spells and Father had a nervous breakdown. But I could NOT objectively say depression runs in my family.

* * *

I don't have to abdicate responsibility for my happiness to some pharmaceutical company in Ohio. I can rely on my own inner strength to keep feeling good. Today I'm putting up an impenetrable barrier against anger and sadness; I won't let them through.

* * *

I crave sex with another woman. Marsha helped me see I don't want a mistress because that would mean one more relationship with someone who could depend on me, as Mother did. What I want is sex with a stranger, without obligation or responsibility, just affection, like an infant gets from his mother, simply because the infant exists. Simply because I exist. It's what Mother denied me. For now, massage will have to do.

* * *

When I was a child, Mother smothered me with her needs. As an adult, when someone expects my emotional support, it's the beginning of the descent into hell.

* * *

Yesterday Sonoma State hired me to teach an overflow accounting class! I met with my students for the first time today. This experience will do me good. I'll manifest my male energy and earn $3,700. That will buy a lot of toys for the son Mother berated because she'd wanted a daughter.

1989

Despite my new job, the period from October last year through this January was one of the blackest I have faced. I had to be self-centered to survive. Taking care of myself had to come first. I didn't have the stamina to deal with people outside the classroom, just barely enough for me. Part-time teaching was my world – it helped sustain me and each day gave a reason to live.

Now that I'm feeling better, I need to lighten up on work and allow room for spontaneity, socializing, and good quality alone time.

* * *

My test whether depression is chemical or situational is this: can I bring myself out of it within an hour or two by sleep, thinking through an issue that troubles me, or exercise?

* * *

Since Desyrel is so unreliable, I'm taking supplements my dietician suggested: vitamin B-complex, vitamin B$_5$, vitamin B$_6$, niacin, biotin, vitamin C, and magnesium. I don't think they are helping in the slightest, even in concert with the antidepressant. And at times they make my heart pound, provoke stomach pain and insomnia, and make me spacey, sedated, hyper, short of breath, and hungry. All my tinkering with nutrient doses has failed. I had such hopes.

* * *

I haven't found a solution and am back where I was several years ago. It's insane to think of having a baby now. Cathy wants to get pregnant and is doomed to frustration. She's bound to resent me more and more because I won't give her what she wants most.

* * *

Recently I've felt vaguely suicidal but, at the same time, calm and peaceful. Depression is still on my mind all the time but it's more a dull ache than a sharp pain.

* * *

The past several days, it seems like hopelessness lurks just below the surface and Desyrel covers it up, like an air freshener conceals a foul odor.

* * *

My new psychiatrist prescribed Prozac in the morning along with Desyrel at bedtime. After a week, my mood has become lighter. Desyrel still helps me sleep. Thanks to Prozac, I hardly ever feel angry and when I do, it's short-lived and quickly forgotten. Sonoma State didn't hire me back because I defiantly wore jeans in the classroom, which my female supervisor (who reminds me of Mother) claimed was unprofessional; I let it slide. But I'm still incredibly sad much of the time and have low energy, blurred vision, and trouble getting an erection.

* * *

I'm preoccupied with extramarital sex. I seem to seek validation as a man. Cathy confirms my virility every day but it's not
enough; I have to find out if other women find me attractive
before I can believe it.

Since Mother treated me as her daughter, all my life I've
doubted my masculinity. I had no father or male adult friend
who would serve as a role model. If a woman finds me sexually attractive, I must be a man. Marsha helped me see the success of a seduction would mean more than the act itself.

* * *

I placed an ad in the personals and twice met Kathleen in my
office for sex. I don't deny excitement and curiosity played a
part. I feel like a traitor, not the husband Cathy deserves. I
love her and don't want her to hurt. She mustn't find out.

1990

When I kick back and relax, despondency hits hard. I have to
stay busy and work fast to keep away the gloom.

Typically, lying around with no motivation whatsoever, I'm
deeply depressed. Then I panic realizing I have a class tonight
to prepare for or have to go to work at my new bookkeeping
job and, presto, my energy improves and so does my mood.

* * *

I feel confined in my marriage. Actually, I'm rebelling against
Mother. When I was small, she invited me into her bed some
mornings and, during the evenings when I was a teenager, she

would parade before me in a flimsy nightgown. She asked me to rub lotion on her bare back. In *Iron Man*, Robert Bly refers to such behavior as "psychic incest." She became jealous when I started dating. She wanted me all to herself.

* * *

Today I took the train to Reno and had sex with a prostitute. I feel some pressure lifted. I do want to continue living with Cathy but need to create space to breathe.

Home again, I'm really enjoying her company. She's a wonderful companion, lover, and friend who has all the qualities I seek in a woman.

* * *

When my spirits sink, I become very young. I honk at drivers who deny me the right of way and curse incompetent sales clerks. Besides throwing tantrums, I lack empathy. And something I'm counting on to make me feel better assumes grand proportions; if it doesn't work out, that constitutes a huge loss. Anything to look forward to is a big deal – if it doesn't materialize, I feel devastated.

* * *

When despondent, I need to accept I'm not going to be my best in the classroom, that I won't be as kind and gentle as usual with Cathy, and that I'll want my way more.

* * *

I landed a tenure-track position teaching auditing at the University of Montana in Missoula, making $48,000 a year! Cathy's excited, too. We're putting our house up for sale.

* * *

Overcome by persistent guilt, I blurted to Cathy about my sexual encounters with Kathleen and the prostitute. Thank God she wants to save our marriage. We've found a therapist for couples counseling.

* * *

I firmly believe much of this depression is stress-induced and so does our therapist. Dejection sets in when I fail to live up to my expectations, like having to correct myself in class after making a mistake.

* * *

Lack of power in my relationship with Cathy is partly responsible for my depression. I feel strangled in our marriage, that she hovers over and absorbs me.

For a time, promiscuity allowed me to reclaim control over my life and destiny. If I'm not in control, Cathy is. Just like Mother was. Just like [my first wife] Barbara was.

* * *

Today my melancholy revolves around lack of connectedness to others, especially men. My illness provides an excuse to put

up barriers, to stay within my shell where life is safe and pre-
dictable, where I don't have to worry about rejection. Where
no one will smother or depend on me. Where I won't hurt.

I won't cut anyone slack. I must have friendships on my terms,
like how often and where we get together. That's an effective
means of keeping others away.

* * *

It's hard to accept what others offer for fear they'll want
something in return. I refuse to become beholden, for I'd feel
guilty taking without reciprocating.

* * *

I'm still seeing Marsha for individual counseling. She says sex
or its possibility is the glue that keeps my relationships together. That's one reason I lack male friends.

Missoula, Montana

We've settled into our new home. I've met my classes and enjoy the challenge of teaching these students, with whom I have
good rapport. But I feel spacey much of each day. I must adjust my supplement doses.

* * *

I'm going to rent some erotic movies and subscribe to *Penthouse*
Magazine and the Playboy Channel. And I'm going to write a
carnal story. I'll indulge in my fantasies this way rather than in
the flesh.

Chapter 3
1991-2000

1991

I must accept I can't be as active as other men my age, and Cathy must, too. Physically I don't have the energy others enjoy and emotionally I constantly deal with stress. So after devoting most of my resources to teaching, I don't have much stamina left.

* * *

I'm planning a night alone at the Travelodge. As much as I love our new home, I need a break from opening mail, reading to-do notes Cathy has left on my desk, breaking up fights between our cats, and cleaning dinner dishes. My teaching load would be bearable if I could shake loose from stress at home.

* * *

I just saw my new therapist. She sees parallels: as with Mother, Cathy's life revolves around me and I'm responsible for her. My wife triggers the same feelings Mother did. There's something wrong in our dynamic; we're all each other has. Also, I see Cathy as I saw Mother: a threat to the development of my social life. Around others, I'm a totally different person when she's not with me.

* * *

I need to recognize my limits as a teacher. Being the best has become a compulsion. In my quest for a five-star rating the first year, I've sacrificed my marriage, friendships, recreation, self-esteem, and peace of mind. I hate the automaton I've become. Cathy is a distraction from my work. While striving for perfection in the classroom, I've failed at everything else.

* * *

Since subscribing to the Playboy Channel, I've become obsessed with pornography. Why? Cathy satisfies me sexually; I don't seek an affair. I believe the reason has to do with Mother. When I was a teenager, masturbating became a symbol for asserting my sexual independence, a way to satisfy my own needs and defy her clandestine overtures. Once while I was bathing with the door locked, she shouted, "You'd better not be doing something in there you're not supposed to!"

Cathy doesn't complain about my watching X-rated movies. Would I experience even more enjoyment if she did? Certainly Mother would have been furious.

* * *

I had one of my Auditing class presentations videotaped. What stuck out was my haughty posture. By appearing superior, I hope to discourage students from asking questions the expert might not be able to answer. I'm a fraud and should not have been placed in a position to teach others material I barely understand myself. A student's observation I contradicted the text confirms my suspicions – he caught me with my pants down. The fact I consistently explain complex material clearly and answer questions accurately doesn't carry weight.

* * *

I've forgotten what it's like to enjoy a conversation without worrying if it's going efficiently, if I'm getting the needed information, and if I'm showing the other person enough interest. Would my attitude be different if I weren't stressed-out most of the time?

* * *

I have a hard time achieving balance. With Cathy, I feel either suffocated or neglected. With work, I'm either swamped or bored. With alone time, I'm either starved for it or lonely.

* * *

I deeply regret not having the option to live a year with my father at age ten or twelve. I would have learned to hunt. I grew up entirely in Mother's realm, living a girl's life, and have never become a man. Having had sessions with three women, I intend to find a male therapist.

* * *

We've decided to have a baby and Cathy is pregnant. I need to become a better person in order to serve as a role model. The timing could be a sign I will overcome this mental illness and live long enough to help raise our child.

* * *

This hopelessness is omnipresent. I'm depressed about the constant depression, which adds to the problem.

* * *

This morning my thoughts are heavy with suicide; I'm grateful for these sleeping pills. I would never have to endure another faculty party feeling scrutinized and awkward or read more cruel course evaluations.

My main concern is abandoning Cathy and our forthcoming child. What if she doesn't remarry? Would it be kinder to do it soon or wait until the baby comes? I can't confide in Cathy – I don't want to worry her. And her reaction could disappoint me; she might take my thoughts lightly and dismiss them.

Afternoon: actually, I'm a long way from following through with this plan. Terramycin, the antibiotic I took to cure bronchitis, caused severe depression, even with Prozac. I've stopped it and might feel better soon.

* * *

Today my problems are teaching-related stress and the inability to relax. I'll cut myself some slack. Although feeling guilty for not living up to my ideal, I've done extremely well holding down a full-time job for over a year despite relentless despondency and physical exhaustion. I have functioned acceptably in the classroom and given Cathy what I could. I must have compassion for myself.

* * *

Initially, taking Desyrel with Prozac worked beautifully. Since then I've tried every reasonable combination and am still depressed. Also, shortness of breath, fatigue, and irregular heartbeat have gotten more pronounced. The medications are providing some relief and I don't dare quit either for fear of feeling worse. The drugs are holding me hostage.

1992

When my back went out Wednesday, it was a sign I needed to ease up prepping for class. It's an emotional barometer. When I let a stressful situation overwhelm me, my body will let me know.

* * *

Early this morning, our daughter, Jeannine Aimée Godwin, was born. Joyful tears are coming frequently. I am listening to two songs that punctuate this experience: "Safe in My Garden" by the Mamas and the Papas and "With the Eyes of a Child" by the Moody Blues. I delivered pink magic markers to four friends and bought a pack of fifty pink paper clips for my own use.

* * *

I saw my new therapist again today and have little respect for him. Repeatedly he makes smart-ass comments and, like Mother, tells me what to do rather than suggests. I want him to treat me with dignity. Are all male therapists like this? I miss Marsha.

* * *

Stress hit hard this week, as bad as it's ever been. Why am I teaching accounting at the University of Montana? It no longer brings enjoyment, just satisfaction my notes are up-to-date and

my handouts, effective. Many hassles, few smiles. Last night I
brought home all my workweek shit and dumped it on Cathy.

Thank God summer vacation is coming. How shall I spend it?
I yearn to get drunk, dance, sing, and fuck my pretty women
students. I'd also like to move to a solitary cabin in the woods
by a creek and railroad tracks. These fantasies help relieve
pressure.

* * *

I really can change my life. I have the choice. I have the
power.

* * *

There's no reason for me to be depressed any longer. Cathy
provides all the nurturing, support, affection, and privacy I desire. Mother is dead.

* * *

It's interesting, attending my new men's therapy group inevitably raises my spirits. And when I become closer to others,
like at the communication workshop several years ago, the
gloom subsides.

* * *

I've stopped both Desyrel and Prozac. When Mother died in
1980 I felt relieved. The day of her funeral my mood was superior. After that, I quit taking antidepressants and stayed off
them for months. Why can't I do the same now?

* * *

We're in Austin, Nevada, on our first day of vacation. When we got here, I was very low. I asked Cathy to hold me and immediately felt better.

* * *

Today I saw my course evaluations from last spring: excellent, my highest yet. This confirms, despite burnout, I'm working in the field best suited to me.

* * *

I'm having a hard time coping this morning. Two months ago, while taking antidepressants, I would have felt paralyzed and bemoaned the fact they weren't working. Today I'm analyzing what caused this misery.

* * *

I've driven to Wallace, Idaho, for the weekend to take a break from school stress. I'm lonely. I miss Cathy and Jenny and want to give Baby her bath.

1993

Yesterday, for the first time, I worked out at the Peak Athletic Club. This weekend I've felt more relaxed than usual and intend to stick to this routine three days each week. My stress level should subside.

* * *

Cathy and I aren't close and haven't made love in ages. I'm jealous of the time she spends with Jenny, the attention and affection she showers on her. We live like roommates. I look forward to when she stops breast-feeding and makes me her body's top priority.

* * *

All afternoon I constantly thought of suicide. This depression is 100% caused by stress. I hate my job, coping with students' needs and demands. I feel trapped. The solution may involve resigning. I cannot work full time and have any kind of personal life, much less help parent our daughter.

Around the time I was born, when he was about 50, my age, Father had a nervous breakdown from overwork in his law practice. He left it and moved to a farm to live alone. I see what could become an eerie parallel.

* * *

After three years of full-time teaching, I've decided to take a leave of absence the spring semester of 1994, from which I will probably not return. I'll have more time to help Cathy with Jenny. Let the transition from wartime to peace begin.

* * *

A great deal of my despondency comes from not getting my way. When things don't go as planned, I become angry at the one preventing it or I run away or I stick around and pout. I should ask myself, "What is it I want and don't have?" Or

"What problem am I avoiding?" Or "What is it I have to do
and don't want to?"

* * *

During the past fourteen months, I've made no progress on my
issues: lack of a central life purpose; burnout from teaching; the
inability to relax or experience pleasure; not feeling close to
anyone, even Cathy and Jenny; and guilt for not giving enough
of myself to my family. I'm just existing, not really living. I'm
ready to try medication again.

* * *

Recently I've found it hard to maintain focus while trying to
solve a problem or hold a conversation. My physician thinks
it's due to not giving my mind a chance to rest. When we talk,
he can tell my brain is always churning and I'm preoccupied.
Certainly this is true; the only time I shut it off is while I sleep.

* * *

I've taken a new antidepressant, Zoloft,[4] four days and have
felt more easy-going and relaxed. I don't take my mental illness quite so seriously. But it hasn't helped much with stress
and at 50 mg, I'm tired and impotent with blurred vision and
nausea. I'll back off to 25.

* * *

---

[4] Selective serotonin reuptake inhibitor (SSRI).

Zoloft is making a tremendous difference in my life. Since
starting it 27 days ago, I haven't thought once of taking my life;
prior to that, it was a daily occurrence. And this week I've
handled stress just fine.

* * *

Although the fall semester just began, yesterday I rented a
small office with large windows and can't wait to furnish it! I
expect to do good work of some kind there when my leave of
absence starts in January. I'm going to take a creative writing
class and want to write a book. Each day I think a little about a
new career.

I ordered business cards: Larry Godwin, Unemployed.

* * *

After taking it two months, I've decided to give up Zoloft. I'm
no longer willing to endure the merciless side effects. I feel
good about this. I'll be on my own again, taking responsibility
for my feelings and behaviors.

* * *

I'm dejected and extremely stressed-out from doing too much.
It's just October, but today I drafted a letter of resignation to
the university, intending to submit it in December.

* * *

I'm anxious about the future. After classes finish, what will I
do? What if inspiration about a new career to pursue with pas-

sion doesn't come? I'll have countless empty hours with no money coming in and my self-esteem is wrapped up in work.

* * *

The fall semester has ended and I did not resign. I won't do it without a firm idea about a new career.

1994

Jenny's just a normal baby but I can't abide her interruptions, crying fits, and independent contrariness. I hate myself when I yell at her. I'd wager Mother couldn't put up with my disruptions, either. I must have learned my reactions from her.

* * *

Yesterday I told my department chair I'm resigning and today announced my decision to the dean. No more fence-sitting or deception. Now I can open myself to discover what I truly desire.

* * *

I am making progress. I'm more patient with Cathy and hardly ever rude to sales clerks and waitresses. It helps to just become aware when I'm about to throw a tantrum and then refuse to excuse it because "I'm depressed." My adult self is finally disciplining my inner child;[5] when I was in grade school, Mother spoiled me and never did.

---

[5] In popular psychology and analytical psychology, the inner child is an individual's childlike aspect. It includes what a person learned

* * *

Pondering our financial situation, I'm becoming queasy. Last year we saved only $10,000 and this year we'll probably lose $30,000. But I must be patient and tolerate the malaise until I'm ready to work again.

* * *

Jenny is my main reason for living. If something should happen to me, Cathy would make out OK but our daughter might not. She needs her daddy. I cherish her more than any other man could.

* * *

I'm really low this morning. It's the same old conflict between loving Cathy and Jenny so much and wanting to spend time with them, versus feeling engulfed by their presence and overwhelmed by responsibility when we're together.

* * *

This permanent sabbatical isn't working out like I'd hoped. Cathy's irate because with all this free time, I don't help more around the house and with Jenny's care. Ironically, although I quit teaching, my obligations have not relented that much.

---

as a child, before puberty. The inner child is often conceived as a semi-independent subpersonality subordinate to the waking conscious mind. The term has therapeutic applications in counseling and health settings. See https://en.wikipedia.org/wiki/Inner_child.

Also, I feel guilty for not working. I'm just as depressed now as a few months ago.

* * *

When I feel suicidal, self-pity overwhelms me. I feel angry that others disappoint me and don't appreciate me enough. When I think of killing myself, I fantasize their reactions: "If only we'd loved him more! If only we'd tried harder to understand him!"

If only Mother had loved me more.

* * *

I need to foster self-forgiveness. When my spirits are deepest, I must acknowledge I'm doing my best.

* * *

Spending so much time alone contributes to my melancholy. It's what Father did to the extent he became a hermit. Yet when other people surround me, I can't wait to get off by myself.

* * *

Despite feeling ashamed to tell others I have no job, I greatly resist work. I need more time to play, more time away from accountability. Although 52, I've never recovered from taking care of Mother as a child. I'm just a boy in a man's clothing.

* * *

Last night, regressing to childhood, I thought, *I'm so sad Daddy doesn't come to see me.* Then immediately I scooped up Jenny, carried her around the house, her arms around my neck, and told her, "I'm very glad to be your daddy."

* * *

I've found a new therapist. Her assignment for me is to sit and observe Cathy and Jenny at various times, their interactions. I'll be able to clearly see what I missed as a child, how it could have been. Then I can grieve that it's too late. No one is ever going to love me like I needed then. I must mourn the part of me that never got hugged, never got listened to, never got respect.

* * *

Despite psychotherapy and extensive journaling, I'm still stressed-out most of the time at home, besieged by my family's requests and demands. Jogging regularly doesn't help much. So I started taking Buspar[6] thirteen days ago and feel a little more relaxed. It may be wishful thinking but, what the hell? Unfortunately, it makes my heart pound, so I'll cut back on the dose.

* * *

These negative self-comparisons with Cathy's dad, the pinnacle of fatherhood, are making my depression worse. I contrast myself to the ideal he exemplifies. When I feel like killing my-

---

[6] An anti-anxiety medication.

self, it's often because of guilt for not measuring up to that standard.

But maybe I'm using the wrong standard. I'm doing a better parenting job than in my first marriage when I deserted my kids. And I'm doing far better than my absent father did with me.

* * *

Buspar isn't working. Ultimately, it hasn't reduced stress or agitation and, at any strength, makes me exhausted and short of breath. I'm discontinuing it.

1995

While single and living in Durango, when feeling despondent, I sought out a friend to talk to and my mood improved. Now, except with Cathy, I keep worries to myself.

* * *

Early this week, to accommodate other tenants who want more space, my office landlord told me I have until March 31 to vacate, although our oral lease doesn't expire until August 31. My attorney assures me the lease is binding and enforceable. Today I told her I will remain here through August. My heart raced, my knees shook, my breath was shallow, and my voice, unsteady. But I did it, then got up and walked out of her office without saying goodbye.

I confronted this pushy, older woman, like Mother, who threatened to trample my rights. I am a man now and need not fear abandonment.

* * *

Today my landlord delivered a letter ordering me to vacate by February 25 or face forcible eviction. This situation has become unbearable. I've decided to place my mental health first, avoid a costly legal fight, and leave. At least I have the satisfaction of standing up to her three days ago.

* * *

I just moved into my new office. The building owner is cordial and my space, quieter. It's situated on the second floor, rather than in the basement like the old one. And the rent is $50 a month lower. Lesson: have faith situations will work out for the best.

* * *

This morning I'm crying because of too much responsibility. Cathy informed me the toilet won't flush. The message I heard was, "You have to fix it." After I did, Little Larry thought, *I'm too young to deal with this! I can't take it anymore!*

I must have felt this way as a child when facing an insurmountable task, with Mommy criticizing me for disappointing her and failing. Her words still echo in my head: "You can't do anything right."

* * *

I phoned my former department chair at U.M. and said I'd like to teach part time next fall. Doing so would provide meaningful work without a full schedule, student advising, committee assignments, or pressure to publish and attend faculty meetings. He offered two sections of Auditing and I agreed to take them. I'll miss my freedom but this ceaseless lethargy has got to end.

* * *

I'm letting Jenny play the sweet tyrant and myself, the willing, complacent victim. I allow her to manipulate me into addressing her wants instead of doing what I'd planned. She makes my home life so miserable I want to flee. It's ironic, our roles seem reversed: she represents Mother thwarting her toddler son with her personal agenda.

* * *

If I forgave Mother, I probably wouldn't become as upset with Cathy and Jenny for the innocent things they do and say that trigger deep-set childhood feelings. Or as angry at the world at large a dozen times a day. But how am I going to do that?

* * *

Although feeling some guilt, I've told Cathy that henceforth in the morning, I will leave for my office when I'm ready without waiting until it's convenient for her and Jenny. And each afternoon, after returning to our chaotic home, I will stake out some alone time with the door closed, even though Jenny's awake. Daddy has taken control.

* * *

My stress level is so high, in desperation, tonight I'm going to restart Desyrel, 50 mg. I stopped taking it three years ago today, just after Jenny was born, when my need was probably greatest.

* * *

After three weeks, I have again abandoned Desyrel because it hasn't helped. I am not going back. And I am not going to feel depressed today.

* * *

My sister-in-law has marital problems and wants to visit. My nephew is very ill. I resent supporting and taking care of other people, including Cathy and Jenny. I can barely take care of myself.

* * *

As I prepare to teach again this fall, stress consumes my life. I decided to try Valium. Initially I felt calmer but, after twelve days, the misery returned along with a pounding heart. Doubling the dose did not help. Another dead end.

* * *

After just two Auditing class meetings, I strongly do not want to continue my career in education. I'm on a treadmill again, enjoying neither the subject matter nor contact with my apathetic students. I already miss my freedom.

* * *

August 30 I started another antidepressant, Serzone. Due to nausea, I backed off from 200 to 150 then 100 mg, but couldn't tolerate even that dose. While taking it, my stress level did go down, but probably that was due to affirmation and disciplining myself to prioritize teaching tasks and do less. So I'm on my own again.

* * *

My doctor prescribed Mellaril, an antipsychotic, thinking it might help with depression. I took one tablet. It caused wave-like nausea, made me irritable, and provoked suicidal thoughts. Then he prescribed Depakote, indicated for bipolar mania, which my body likewise rejected. Damn.

* * *

I'm doing my best to balance my life: family, students, and self. I'm trying to keep all the balls as high in the air as possible and failing miserably. I treat Cathy and Jenny shamefully. I sacrifice everyone to get as much prep work done as quickly as possible.

* * *

At lunch today, a vivid image appeared. Someone hammered a small version of myself into a square hole with a wooden mallet. I tried to accommodate the space but could not fit. I looked up to see who was driving the mallet down on my head: a large version of myself.

* * *

I remember hearing God doesn't give us a heavier weight than we can bear, and over the years that has seemed true for me. But what about those who kill themselves? Do they have hidden resources they don't know about? Or does the rule not apply to depression?

* * *

Classes have ended. I'm going to survive.

1996

Maybe I'm making excuses, but if the sun came pouring through my office window, I'd feel more cheery. I long to meander to lunch in my shorts. To some extent, the weather dictates my moods.

* * *

I've started writing a book, consisting of excerpts from my journals about my childhood. It might help heal wounds left from that period. Also, the project is becoming a way of connecting with those I tell about it.

* * *

As I write, memories of hyper-responsibility and engulfment arise. It's not a matter of forgetting Mother's abuse; I don't need to do that. I want to stop reliving it.

* * *

I hate everyone. I especially hate selfish people who try to hinder and control me, like Mother did. I hate my life and would like to cash out.

* * *

I don't want others to see me struggle. I'm proud of the fronts that mask my low spirits. Those facades are practiced and very effective.

* * *

I'm feeling dejected this morning. I just heard that the grandfather of my three-year-old friend slapped him and called him stupid for falling off a swing. This reminds me of my own pain at his age. The event is therapeutic. I need to absorb it and move on.

* * *

Writing my book is beneficial. After spending an hour or two editing a chapter in the morning, I usually feel alive and less troubled the rest of the day.

* * *

Working on my book and encountering more horrid reminders from childhood, yesterday I reached the point of either finding a new antidepressant or doing away with myself. But I may instead try some more supplements, which might not cause debilitating side effects.

Yet this evening I have a new perspective. For twelve years, I made my illness worse by taking medications AND supplements my body wouldn't tolerate longer than a few days. It screamed, "Hey, I've had enough screwing around. Leave me alone." Why would it have changed?

* * *

Barbara phoned at 6:15 this morning to say, at 27, David drowned in South Korea. I'm so sad I didn't nurture him as a toddler and young man when he needed me, and could never make up for what I denied him. I feel guilty, too, but in my defense, I later apologized for my neglect, then provided some financial support and told him I loved him. I must forgive myself for abandoning him. Considering, at the time, my immaturity and the absence of a father to serve as a role model, perhaps I did my best.

* * *

I've felt more helpless and overwhelmed by responsibility since Jenny was born. This may pass as she grows older. Right now we lead parallel lives; she's the inadvertent catalyst of recollections of the mistreatment I suffered at her age. But comforting her when she feels hurt or scared helps me heal.

1997

Since Cathy and Jenny returned from Sacramento after Christmas, I resent sharing our home and this has been a major contributor to depression. How I miss my solitary mornings and evenings when the house was quiet and all mine! Now, many times each day the thought comes, *I wish I lived alone.*

* * *

I feel so dispirited reading accounts of cruelty to children and animals. I'm powerless to prevent such abuse. The most likely way I could contribute to making the world safer is to finish my book and find a publisher. Maybe people who commit atrocities come from dysfunctional families that breed unhealthy childhoods. If I could help avert one murder or suicide, that would mean much more than helping someone pass the CPA exam.

* * *

The most important thing I did yesterday happened after Jenny broke the plate under the dinner candle. She cowered and looked like she might cry. I swept her up and she clung to me tightly. Then I held her on my lap and gave her an M&M. Contrast my reaction to the time Mother blew up after I tipped over the cigar stand and ruined it, and her spanking me when I got lost while we were shopping.

* * *

I'm extremely low this morning. The way I live my life isn't working. Although 54 years old, I'm stuck emotionally reacting to everything that goes wrong as a little boy would. I don't evaluate situations objectively.

* * *

As despondent as I am, it's important to keep living. It's important that I continue to make Cathy's and Jenny's lives easier.

* * *

I'm writing my chapter on forgiveness and will try to see my childhood from Mother's point of view. My grandmother was cold and did not display affection, so Mother lacked a role model. Having already given birth to two sons over a decade earlier, she pined for a daughter to spoil and help complete her own unhappy childhood. Father broke her heart when he left. Mother did not make friends easily and we had no relatives close by. She was bogged down by a new child's diapers to change, with no emotional pillar and questionable finances during wartime. She lived in survival mode but provided me with food, clothing, and medical attention. Lonely, she slept in my room and kept me home all she could. She shouldered me with responsibility because I was the only one available. Unthinking and needy, she considered me not only her caregiver but her partner. She was mentally unstable and remained untreated. It never crossed her mind she was abusing me. Can't I acquit her?

* * *

Having walked a mile in his shoes, this morning I feel compassion for Father and forgive him. With his nervous condition, parenting a new son must have seemed impossible. And giving up his law practice probably devastated him. It's somewhat the same for me with teaching.

I feel sad we didn't have a father-son relationship, that he wouldn't let himself receive the love I'd have freely given.

* * *

As a child, I experienced no intimacy. As an adult, I find opportunities every day but block it. Why? I think it's because intimacy involves obligation and can lead to engulfment. I'm not equipped to endure either; both can lead to suicidal thoughts.

* * *

I've started Serzone again. In 1995 my body couldn't tolerate it but after two weeks, now it does.

* * *

We're on summer vacation at Glacier National Park and I fantasize killing myself. The heater in this cheerless, mosquito-infested motel room doesn't work; the smoky, noisy restaurants have uncomfortable chairs and employ inept servers; and I feel trapped in this cage with my family. I miss my routines and am counting the days until we return home.

I've given Cathy notice I won't take her and Jenny on a vacation next year without getting myself in better shape psychologically.

* * *

I've taken Serzone a month and wonder if it's making my depression worse. My body continues to accept it but during this period, my moods have nosedived. Is it messing with my brain? Maybe not. I decided to up my dose from 300 to 450 mg.

* * *

I've blown up at Cathy and Jenny twice recently and seem generally more volatile since starting Serzone. I'm going to discontinue it. I'll never be sure it was the right decision but this I know: it's not helping.

* * *

Jenny started kindergarten this morning. I'm so happy for her. She's getting an experience Mother forbade me because of "all the sickness going around."

* * *

I'm sending book proposals to 27 traditional publishers. If one doesn't accept my manuscript, I'll pay perhaps $5,000 to a subsidy publisher to print and distribute it. I've worked too hard and long to see this project die.

* * *

I've just read *Winter Blues* by Norman Rosenthal. Today I crave sunshine. Possibly my depression around Christmas has something to do with seasonal affective disorder.[7] But I doubt it. Christmas intensifies my issues: longing for intimacy; stifling confinement; disruptions in my routines; and obligations to buy, wrap, and mail gifts, then react favorably to the ones I

---

[7] Seasonal affective disorder is a type of depression that relates to changes in the seasons. Typically SAD symptoms begin in the fall and continue through the winter months. The reduced level of sunlight may cause SAD, disrupting the body's internal clock and causing a drop in serotonin, a brain chemical that can affect mood. See https://www.mayoclinic.org/diseases-conditions/seasonal-affective-disorder/symptoms-causes/syc-20364651.

receive. To cope, I stay solitary and aloof but project the persona I'm happy and all's well. I've considered running away but can't bear the thought of spending Christmas Eve in a motel room. So this year I'm flunking again, missing out on what others enjoy and I deserve: connection and peace.

1998

Considering the abuse I suffered as a child, all my adult behavior is normal, and I accept my conduct as long as it does not hurt others or interfere with their rights. This includes avoiding, as much as possible, situations that require responsibility for fixing things at home that go wrong and for taking care of my family. It also means spending most of my time alone, away from people who would confine me, and involves refusing to allow others to control my decisions. I feel no guilt.

* * *

It's time to grow up. To overcome this despondency, I must own that I am a man, not a child. Situations that debilitated me when I was young don't have to any longer.

* * *

Feedback from my therapists says I should have responded to my extensive inner child work by now. Surely I have a problem with endogenous depression[8] and will again try to find a medication or supplement to fix it.

---

[8] Endogenous depression seemingly occurs for no reason, and appears to be chemical and/or genetic in nature. On the other hand, exogenous, or reactive-situational, depression is usually triggered by some sort of outside stressor, like the loss of a loved one, rejec-

This funk has deepened the last few days with no link whatsoever to outside events. Nothing cheers me up. If the mailman delivered an acceptance letter from a publisher, I'd feel no less down.

* * *

Last night on the phone with her aunt, Cathy said, "Larry's the only one in the family who's managed to stay healthy. He's doing fine." I wanted to blurt, "Last week I felt like killing myself. You think you have problems?"

But my silence, sparing Cathy and Jenny the truth, was a precious gift. I made the right decision to keep my mouth shut.

* * *

Like the others, Strawberry Hill rejected my book proposal. I'm very discouraged. No one wants to publish my work.

* * *

As a result of writing my book, I've achieved a great deal of clarity about the childhood origins of my problems with responsibility, confinement, and insecurity. Taking into account my degree of enlightenment and the steps I've taken to address

---

tion, divorce, losing a job, or relationship difficulties. It generally resolves once the individual is able to adapt to the situation. Modalities to treat both types of major depression include medication and psychotherapy. See https://www.verywellmind.com/what-is-endogenous-depression-1067283 and https://en.wikipedia.org/wiki/Adjustment_disorder.

these issues, why don't I feel less depressed? Events that trigger the issues devastate me as much today as they did four years ago.

* * *

I've been playing "let's pretend" with others and myself. Let's pretend Larry is normal. Let's pretend he has no long-term psychological concerns that could interfere with doing what others want, like taking long vacations with his family and welcoming houseguests. I'd better drop the pretense, level with everyone, and make decisions that are best for me. Otherwise I risk reaching the breaking point and committing suicide. Surely everyone who cares about me would agree with my resolution.

* * *

Thank God Dimi Press, a subsidy publisher, has agreed to take on my book. The title will be *Surviving Our Parents' Mistakes*. I put my check and our signed contract in the mail today. Although I have to pay the cost, at last my efforts will see print next spring.

* * *

The reason I enjoy women's company more than men's, and have mostly female friends, is they seem more sensitive and feeling-oriented, like I am. They're more apt to identify with, support, and nourish me.

* * *

Last night Cathy and I watched the movie *Disaster in Time*. At the end, the father rescued his daughter from her grandparents, who had kidnapped her. Afterward I vividly recalled thinking, as a child, *My daddy's going to come and take me away.*

* * *

For several years I've felt dejected after each get-together with our two best friends and wondered, *What's wrong with me*? The thought never entered my brain they had changed and I might re-evaluate the friendship.

* * *

This year I've experimented with many health food supplements, including the hormone melatonin, various vitamins and minerals, amino acids, and herbal remedies like St. John's wort. All but two made my distress worse. Calcium-magnesium does reduce my endogenous depression. 5-HTP seems to improve my stress-induced despondency but apparently blocks cal-mag's benefit, so I stopped taking it. I can't win.

1999

Tonight I'll return home from my office and again have nothing to share with Cathy and Jenny about my day. They'll tell me about their activities and adventures, and I'll listen and make a comment or two. I'm so weary of my sedentary, stagnant life.

* * *

I've had several confrontations with another tenant on my office building floor about the noise she creates by leaving her door open while she talks with clients, and where to set the heat thermostat. Today she called me an asshole and said she feels sorry for Jenny that I'm her dad. She added, "I can see why you've had so much trouble in your life."

I'm angry but will not react as she expects because I don't want to escalate our conflict. I have my space heater on and am quite comfortable. Its sound helps drown out her noise, too. I refuse to give her power. This is new territory for me: I can live with disharmony without fear. Besides that, her insults shouldn't matter. I know I'm a good person, a good parent.

* * *

I feel like a violet standing alone in a vast meadow. When a cool, gentle breeze blows, I feel peaceful. If the wind turns strong and hot from the south, I plot suicide.

* * *

This afternoon I took a rose to my volatile office neighbor. At first she seemed mad, then said, "Very touched. Thank you very much." We'll probably never be friends again but the tension between us should decline. Is the 5-HTP I restarted making me calmer?

* * *

The 5-HTP benefit, if any, didn't last. I'm back on the ideal slate of antidepressants and supplements: none!

* * *

My first 500 copies of *Surviving Our Parents' Mistakes* will arrive tomorrow. I'm savoring this triumph, over three years in the making. Now, on to promotion.

* * *

The issues I fret about while dejected are real and valid. But this illness exploits weaknesses in my most vulnerable areas, and magnifies problems so they dominate my thinking and incapacitate me.

* * *

Why have I become so sensitive to small doses of medications and supplements? A few months ago I tolerated 500 mg of calcium-magnesium a day. Now just five mg make me depressed. I suspect the problem results from abusing my body with so many ineffective supplements over the last three years.

* * *

It's important to trust my dietary cravings. When I yearn for meat or chocolate and ignore it, my moods usually deteriorate soon after. Both contain amino acids that break down into neurotransmitters, such as norepinephrine, which has the potential to combat sadness and apathy, and serotonin, which can reduce stress and anger. I'm going to eat a generous portion of meat at each of my three meals and dark chocolate at least once a day. Since I'm no longer taking pills, diet is my only tool to head off depression.

* * *

Despite protein loading, I still often feel dispirited. This morning I'm restarting both calcium-magnesium, which apparently boosts norepinephrine, and 5-HTP, which increases serotonin.

* * *

The trouble with low doses of medications and supplements is when hopelessness returns, I don't know if I'm taking too much or not enough.

* * *

Cathy and I had a painful conversation this morning. I told her I feel neglected and she said my struggle with depression is hard on her. The main problem is my inconsistency; I'm like two different people. When I walk in the door, she never knows if my mood will be fair or foul.

* * *

For the second time, I've stopped both calcium-magnesium and 5-HTP because neither improved my mood consistently and both caused irritating side effects. I'm on my own again.

2000

This is my third morning drinking decaf (which still retains two to three percent caffeine) instead of real coffee. I feel drugged and sleepy but less stressed-out than usual. Evidently too much caffeine doesn't agree with me, but a certain amount, from decaf and chocolate, exerts an antidepressant effect.

* * *

Last night Cathy and I had a heated discussion about whether or not she should resign as trustee of her father's estate, as one of her older sisters insists. Jenny, who was listening, said, "I'm glad I'm just a kid." Her remark opened a wound. When I was eight, Mother burdened me with her problems, expecting me to understand and take her side.

* * *

Almost every time something at home breaks and it's my job to fix it, I can choose when to do so. Often I want closure and tackle it right away, but a better tactic would be to exercise self-discipline and wait until later when I might feel less tired and stressed-out. Seldom is the problem a crisis that requires immediate attention. I can control my timing.

* * *

I'm not good enough for Cathy and Jenny and feel guilty I can't be what they want. They deserve so much better. Taking my life would free them to find a proper adult who would relish spending weekends at home, attending Jenny's piano recitals and sharpening her pencils, and taking his family on frequent vacations without complaining. I'm selfish to deny them that opportunity.

On the other hand, I make a positive difference in their lives every day. I roughhouse with Jenny on the couch; record movies we enjoy watching together; act "the monster" while giving her a bath; play fun, educational games with her on the computer; encourage her creative writing; drive her to school each morning; and kiss her at bedtime every night. For Cathy, I run errands; wash dinner dishes; fix appliances that stop working, when I have the expertise; take her out to dinner occasionally; and listen when she's sick, troubled, or sad.

I don't give my family all they want but I give them what they need: support, reassurance, security, and affection. My performance isn't black or white.

* * *

It's my birthday and I'm critical of the gifts my family and friends gave me. They could have done more. If I walked into a hall where 10,000 people sang "Happy Birthday," I'd wonder why some didn't attend.

Surely it's because Mother didn't fuss over me this special day. But no one can ever make up for the attention I missed then. I can only enjoy and appreciate what others give me now.

* * *

A week has passed since my birthday and I just reread my cards. I feel blessed many caring people remembered me so generously. They gave me lots of attention, too. And I really like my gifts, can't find fault with any of them. I'm grateful to see this situation now through an adult's lens rather than that of a pouting child.

* * *

Depression hit hard yesterday after taking prednisone for
asthma, then going off it. Resolved: I will never again consider
that drug except in a life-threatening situation.

* * *

These days Cathy constantly requires my nurturing for ongoing health problems and family issues that have recently arisen.
Here I am again, taking care of a needy adult woman. She's
about the same age as Mother when she made me her sole
caregiver.

* * *

Tonight I seem incredibly lucky. Every day Jenny graces me
with her presence and I bask in her and Cathy's love. I'm seldom depressed and my physical health is good. Thanks to the
stock market, at this time neither Cathy nor I have to work. We
live in a beautiful home in a quiet neighborhood in a community where we feel at peace. I didn't have this much good for-
tune living alone in Corvallis.

Chapter 4
2001-2010

2001

I'm on a runaway roller coaster, physically and mentally. There's absolutely no pattern, no predictability to the way I feel from one hour to the next. The apparent randomness is wearing me down.

* * *

My life is barren in three areas: interpersonal relationships, work, and personal growth. For this thought to occur to me is an encouraging sign, as if I might soon have the mental capability to change.

* * *

I just read my 1975 diary from Corvallis and feel very sad. I had so much mental and physical energy compared to now. Since 1980 I've depleted my resources by taking megadoses of antidepressants and supplements and will probably never be the same. But maybe if I scrupulously avoid pills from now on, my condition could go back to the way it was.

* * *

At nine, Jenny has gotten so much easier to live with. And these days, having decided to forgive Mother, I no longer dwell on her abuse. My stress level should decline.

* * *

When depressed, I feel abnormal and guilty wanting to spend almost all my free time alone. But when my spirits are high, I accept I'm a strong introvert.

* * *

In the midst of this despondency, I'm not responsible for my feelings. I can't talk myself out of irritability and apathy. But I am accountable for my behavior, for cracks in my facade.

* * *

My brain is like an orchestra composed of rebellious instruments, my metaphor for neurotransmitters. Each plays isolated, arbitrary, discordant notes with no conductor.

* * *

Today I began my Christmas grieving. I bought three seasonal CDs and listened to one, a children's choir singing carols. Probably the more I mourn what I missed as a child at this time of year, the more I'll come to embrace the wonder and anticipation Jenny enjoys.

2002

Bored with my vegetative existence, I'm teaching one section of Accounting Principles at the university this semester. Stress overwhelmed me when I taught there before but I resolve to no longer play the victim. I must take control of my life. I'll pace myself on workdays and exercise restraint when I need rest. I can do this.

* * *

I'm suicidally depressed again coping with home responsibilities and my family's neediness, which I've journaled about
countless times. I may not have long to live. This gives me li-
cense to splurge on purchases and activities that give momen-
tary pleasure, and to postpone checkups for my eyes, skin, and
prostate. These liberating thoughts offer some consolation.

* * *

Today I hit rock bottom but didn't busy myself with activity to
take my mind off it, like I usually do. I allowed myself to sink
as deep as possible. It's like an infection: let it run its course
and be done with it. Rising, I felt cleansed.

* * *

I'm pushing the river by continuing to teach at U.M. I'm so
sour about my lazy, insolent, arrogant students, my motivation
is suffering. My feelings this semester reinforce the decision to
leave I made twice before; I don't belong here any longer. After the term ends, I must have trust a worthwhile project will
emerge to fill the void.

* * *

My counselor thinks my morose moods come from Mother's
indulgence to compensate for her neglect, which fostered
grandiosity and narcissism. So my therapy work seems to have
backfired. I've pampered my inner child and now must put
him on an extinction schedule. Whenever a confrontation between him and my adult comes up, my adult will prevail.

* * *

Two days ago, I started Effexor-XR, prescribed for both depression and anxiety. But I've stopped it because of impotence, which would likely become stronger the longer I took it. Sex is too enjoyable a part of my life to give up, plus it helps alleviate stress. I'll return to facing my mental problems without intervention.

* * *

This depression is insidious. I seldom know for certain whether it's endogenous or stress-induced.

* * *

I'm frustrated and angry about events beyond my control. Bush will probably attack Iraq; the stock market indices hit new lows today; and this year, already we've had to replace our well pump, water softener, and furnace. I'm really worried about our finances.

* * *

I've just come from Jenny's piano recital and am very low. Everyone else smiled and laughed and seemed connected to one another. In my solitary world with its barriers, I felt so different, just like in Durango, desperately longing to be normal.

* * *

I miss involvement. While teaching last semester, I was stressed-out but felt a sense of accomplishment. And last month I wasn't dispirited editing a client's book, thanks to the new business I started. But now I have no projects on the horizon.

* * *

As I look back over melancholy times since 1979, many related to regrets over life choices and longing for former circumstances that were surely happier. I was never satisfied. Recollections became a series of fantasies as I desperately wished to regain what I'd lost.

* * *

I've mourned my childhood enough. Hell, I've been doing it for decades. My grieving has been way out of proportion to the importance early memories should occupy in my adult life. I'm through sulking.

2003

This afternoon I attended Jenny's winter piano recital. I felt so much more present and friendly than after her November one. The reasons are I'm no longer prodding myself to do too much; I've stopped taking harmful supplements; and I carefully watch my diet, especially decaf and chocolate for the optimal amount of caffeine.

* * *

I've had it with this fucking depression. This is the fourth day and I'm calling time. I'm doing everything right and deserve to feel good.

But it's not that simple. I cannot will myself out of this mood.
I must be patient. Bear the discomfort and comfort will come.

* * *

I felt dejected all morning until after lunch, when I devoured a
huge chocolate chip cookie. Suddenly the gloom disappeared!

* * *

Today I'm angry for having this mental illness while most others do not. It's not fair! I feel so peculiar, but that doesn't
make me a bad person. I don't choose to be this way. I do love
many people and permit them to love me as much as I'm able.
It's a solace knowing Cathy and Jenny accept me despite my
limitations.

* * *

This rage at the rude driver comes from my inner child, who
has not forgiven Mother for her abuse. My adult has done so
on an intellectual level but my emotional child calls the shots.

* * *

For three years, feeling sorry for myself because of this disorder has been a major life theme. I dwelled on it excessively and
wasted time because there's nothing I can do about it.

* * *

Around the time Mother died in 1980, I took the tricyclic antidepressant Norpramin, which boosts norepinephrine. It didn't

help with deep stress-induced depression but maybe it would relieve the endogenous type. I've decided to try it again. Thinking I can cure this despondency without medication is another example of my grandiosity.

* * *

I started taking 25 mg Norpramin three nights ago. Since then, my mood has stayed 9 on my scale of 1 (worst) to 10. Could it be a placebo effect? Maybe not. But I felt sedated, spacey, anxious, and constipated, so cut the tablet in half. My plan is to find and maintain a therapeutic dose and hope my body will adapt to the side effects.

* * *

I'm still in the Norpramin honeymoon phase, and for thirteen days it's felt like summer vacation. But although the drug seems to have fixed endogenous depression, even a low dose makes me stressed-out.

* * *

I bought a book about posttraumatic stress disorder (PTSD) and it seems like I'm reading about myself. I haven't grieved my abusive childhood enough nor discharged my anger against Mother. And I've chosen to relive my childhood with Cathy as my new mom. I'm going to talk to others about my trauma, journal more extensively, and ask my therapist about PTSD recovery.

* * *

I've written a short story recounting my childhood with a different ending. Accidentally, I kill Mother by pushing her down the stairs after she spanked me. Then the kind, childless lady across the street invites me to live with her. Each time I read it, tears overcome me.

* * *

A fire has erupted on Black Mountain and last night we had to evacuate to a motel. I haven't fallen apart but feel like a little boy again. Cathy and Jenny are handling it fine, but I'm scared and desperately miss our home and my routines.

* * *

At our session yesterday, my therapist used the eye movement desensitization and reprocessing (EMDR) technique,[9] highly recommended for PTSD sufferers. Unfortunately, I still feel as helpless and angry as before. I'm giving up on it.

* * *

After the Idaho Writer's League meeting in Coeur d'Alene, I felt vacant and alone. I'm still the outsider. I've retreated because of depression and forgotten how to enjoy others' com-

---

[9] Eye movement desensitization and reprocessing is a form of psychotherapy developed by Francine Shapiro in the 1990s in which the person being treated is asked to recall distressing images. The therapist then directs the client by using side-to-side eye movements or hand tapping. See https://en.wikipedia.org/wiki/Eye_movement_desensitization_and_reprocessing.

pany. But now that my gloom has subsided, the past doesn't have to limit me any longer. I can become more sociable if I choose.

* * *

I'm a science experiment gone awry. Trying to relieve stress, I tinkered with several new supplements and they backfired. So I'm in bad shape again and cannot trust my emotions, especially anger. Trying to justify it based on external events is inappropriate. I must resist the temptation to act on unreliable feelings.

2004

Before dinner Cathy fussed over Jenny's nosebleed much more than she does over me when I feel depressed. She must love Jenny more.

* * *

I'm especially sensitive right now, a Norpramin side effect, and that influences my journaling as I magnify my problems. I took only 2.5 mg last night and won't take any tonight. Maybe my brain has topped up its norepinephrine stores and I don't need the drug any longer.

* * *

I've been off Norpramin ten days, am despondent again, and will restart it tonight. I cannot figure the drug out.

* * *

It's obvious I brought on this current misery by agonizing over our upcoming trip to Spokane to visit Cathy's aunt and uncle. Norpramin does NOT fix stress-induced depression. Again, I'm stopping the drug.

* * *

Last night Jenny brought me a tiny bouquet of flowers she picked and my mood brightened.

* * *

Yesterday someone told me we each have to play the hand we're dealt. Walking to lunch today, I helped steady a woman who has cancer. She passed out while driving her car after a chemo treatment. She can't trade her hand for another and neither can I. We must both do our best with the capabilities we have and, given the choice, I prefer depression to cancer.

* * *

Medication and psychotherapy don't help everyone. Mental hospitals brim with people like me who don't completely respond to either. There they live without freedom, autonomy, or privacy. And physically, I could be bound to a wheelchair. Or I could be dead. I'm lucky to live and function as well as I do.

* * *

It's probably a blessing medications for stress-induced depression don't help me. This forces me to solve personal problems using my own resources, which can empower and foster self-esteem.

2005

Today I received an e-mail reply from [my 37-year-old daughter] Andrea saying she's "not interested in reestablishing a relationship with me at this time." Although we've been distant since her brother died in 1996, I'd hoped that would change. She hasn't sent me a Father's Day card in years. I've lost both my adult children.

I feel hurt Andrea no longer loves me but if she's happy, that's a compensation. I'm again including her in my nightly prayers. Thank God I have one daughter who cares for me.

* * *

Hoping to lower my stress level, I took Xanax again fifteen days and it's made me despondent. Advice to myself: Don't take anything seriously. Retreat when I start to feel rocky. Realize, since I'm off the drug, this imbalance should work itself out within a few days.

* * *

I took aspirin and ibuprofen for low-back pain and bursitis in my hip. The pills made me depressed. This time I will not reach for Norpramin; patience will cure this discomfort.

* * *

Now that my moods have brightened, I feel frustrated my life lacks passion. I'm just existing. Feeling content doesn't make it; I crave excitement.

But exhilaration sneaks up on me: after jogging especially fast; once I've solved a difficult computer problem; and when something I've written sparkles.

* * *

In desperation, I made an appointment with a naturopath who prescribed pituitary and thyroid gland extracts to help me manage stress. I took them, separately, very dilute, for six days. Like all the other supplements I've tried, they didn't help and my body could not abide the side effects. When will I learn?

* * *

When particularly stressed-out, sometimes I journal very little, just when I need it most. I don't take time to look within to see how the big picture interfaces with the little things I need to attend to.

* * *

I just caught myself getting depressed because my sister-in-law will arrive from California tomorrow. I dread the disruptions in the routines that anchor and sustain me. We haven't had a houseguest in ten years! No wonder this is a big deal. I must plan ahead and have compassion for myself.

* * *

I desperately want to make up for my rotten childhood, to re-live it and make it right. I want to win in the present what I missed then: love, space, and security. Thanks to her mother and me, Jenny's getting everything I deserved – I'm envious and angry about the injustice.

* * *

I cannot overcome the mental effects of genes apparently in-herited from my parents, but I can adapt my lifestyle to live with them. By doing so, I experience some pleasure most days.

* * *

This Christmas, rather than berate myself for failing, I'll give myself credit for what I do, the activities I undertake trying to make the season joyful for my family. It's my gift to them, in-finitely more than Father did, living alone on his farm.

2006

Last night Cathy and I talked and now we realize why we're not close. She hasn't forgiven me for treating her badly during my most depressed period, 1994-2000. I never abused her, physically or mentally, but was angry, critical, and in a bad mood much of that time. Although I've apologized and now behave lovingly, she still feels resentful.

* * *

By masking my mental illness, I get along with almost every-one. Although the odd duck, I honor society's rules. No one else could imagine my mind's interior.

* * *

Enough complaining about things going wrong. Lately I look forward to getting up every day and am rarely despondent. Let's get some perspective here: I'm feeling so much better than during most of the last 23 years! Compared to that time, this is heaven.

* * *

My back is so sore, I can't jog, and skin cancer surgery looms tomorrow. Some relief comes from simply writing down these anxieties and facing them.

* * *

Ultrasensitivity hampers my ability to function and enjoy life. Although most things are going great, when a trivial trigger occurs, like someone's rude remark, I lose sense of proportion and my mood plummets. Or it soars when somebody compliments me unexpectedly. Sensitivity makes me a more proficient writer but it wreaks havoc with my emotions.

* * *

An ongoing conflict embroils me: the man I am vs. the one I was and long to be again. I'm often either stressed-out or depressed, not the energetic, gregarious, even-tempered person Cathy married. I do inhabit that former man's brain for short periods but, because of mental illness, I must accept my inability to do all he could, as well as this current need for solitude. I still accomplish a lot and enjoy others' company, albeit briefly. These two men have much in common.

* * *

Now my overall goal is not to reclaim the health I've lost but to continue living. To reach this objective, I must make smart choices, like refusing to dwell on conflicts with others, becoming more tolerant, honoring my limits when trying to please my family, eating wisely, and simplifying my life.

* * *

I still have a long way to go to forgive Mother, my only pathway to peace. Every day I allow repressed anger to infect my relations with someone, especially while driving. I act out that anger on innocent bystanders and it harms me as well as them. Mother is dead. I must acknowledge my childhood is over and I can never avenge those wrongs.

2007

I'm no longer ashamed to tell others about my suicidal thoughts. They're a part of who I am. My friends will still accept me and I don't care about the rest.

* * *

I'm rereading *The Highly Sensitive Person* by Elaine Aron. It's a therapeutic way to reframe my emotional upheavals and validates what I feel, so I don't seem so abnormal. It uplifts my spirits to encounter myself in her writing and engenders self-compassion.

* * *

I am a good person, just very needy. I need more love.

* * *

I take life one day at a time. Today I choose to live.

* * *

Cathy broke her ankle and just had surgery. I'm doing as much as I can to help her, considering my stress level. Our neighbors and her friends, who notice my absence during the day, probably think I'm self-centered and don't love my wife. I do feel guilty for not doing more, but that beats taking my life to prove them wrong.

* * *

My longtime friend suggests I adopt Christianity to relieve depression. Why do I strongly resist organized religion? My disdain comes from pressure to conform. I do pray to God and believe I have a personal relationship with Him, that He probably loves me. That's enough.

* * *

I've rented the vacant office next to mine and plan to furnish it like an apartment (minus kitchen). It will provide a tranquil space when I'm tired of working, and will make it easy to spend one night a week away from our chaotic home. Cathy approves of the idea.

* * *

For three days I took the MAO inhibitor Eldepryl, hoping to lower my anxiety. It didn't and my mood collapsed. I need Norpramin again.

* * *

Life is good. Sticking to my diet has reduced stress. I love my new office suite and find enjoyment there and elsewhere every day. I feel grateful to live with Cathy and Jenny, to receive their love and give it back. I feel blessed for my writing creativity and our financial security. Now the imperatives are to neither clutter my life by doing too much nor spoil it by trying new medications.

* * *

I've reached another low point this morning. We were supposed to celebrate Father's Day last night but Cathy dropped the ball. My relationship with [teenage] Jenny is practically nonexistent anyway; Mom is her buddy, not Dad. And Andrea still wants nothing to do with me. Is all this because I'm such a marginal father?

* * *

Many times I awaken from my afternoon nap feeling tired and apathetic. It occurs after I've worked too hard during the morning or the previous day, or am otherwise uptight. My body says, "Hold up, pardner. I just want to rest."

* * *

Andrea wrote today to thank me for my birthday card. She
said she'll write again soon and signed her message "Love."
This is wonderful news.

* * *

One of our writing group members delivered a scathing critique of my story and spoke in a singsong voice, like she was
addressing a child. But she made some excellent suggestions
for improvement. I need to develop a thicker skin. Beyond
that, I must forgive *myself* for failing to exercise tact when in-
teracting with others. Although meaning well, sometimes I
inadvertently hurt someone's feelings.

* * *

My doctor injected a steroid into my swollen sternoclavicular
joint. First it made me hyper and edgy, then deeply depressed.
Thank God for Norpramin.

2008

I taped a Nikken magnet to my sternoclavicular joint, hoping to
reduce swelling. It did not but instead made me despondent. I
can't believe my body is this sensitive. I need Norpramin
again.

* * *

I feel sad Jenny and I spend so little time together and that I
don't participate more in her life. But if I were dead, I
wouldn't participate at all. Then, if someone asked what her
father was like, she'd probably say, "I didn't really know him."

* * *

I feel hurt Andrea writes only twice a year. In her last message she said, "I'm so busy. We need to go slow as we reestablish our relationship." I suspect her sole reason for staying in touch is to manipulate me into leaving her a bequest after I die. If so, she has a stake in my suicide.

* * *

I'm so grateful for my office and suite, this private space that shuts others out. Without it I doubt I could keep living.

* * *

Running virus scans is therapeutic. Watching my computer methodically check each file suggests there's a pattern to life and perhaps I can solve my problems by approaching them systematically.

* * *

I feel despondent and irritable. Just now I spoke rudely to a server at Food for Thought. Here's my advice: forgive yourself, accept it, and move on. Apologize tomorrow if you think it's necessary.

* * *

I've been off Norpramin over two months and am still not depressed. So much to be thankful for.

2009

Here's my New Year's resolution to manage stress, the three P's: Review my list of tasks and *pass* on the nonessential ones. *Prioritize* the ones that remain. Of those, *postpone* the ones that can wait.

* * *

I can't relax because I don't know how. I stay busy, often doing meaningless "work." While watching a movie, I look at the elapsed time to determine when it will end. In their free hours, other men play golf and travel the country in their RVs. Mother didn't teach me to relax because she didn't know how. Can I learn this skill?

* * *

With Cathy and Jenny, I feel like a service animal valued for what I do, not who I am. Neither includes me in conversation by taking an interest in my activities or feelings. I don't have a say in decision-making. When we quarrel, Cathy consistently takes Jenny's side. I'm the outsider but too angry to kill myself.

* * *

Tonight I told Jenny about my frustrations. She listened and the tension between us has lifted. From now on, I will do everything possible to nurture my relationship with the daughter who loves me.

* * *

I am responsible for my happiness. If I'm not happy, I need to do something differently.

* * *

Last night Cathy and I talked. She's upset because I'm a perfectionist, wanting things my way and just so. She pointed out I criticize her every day for mistakes she makes while cooking and for her oversights. We hardly ever do anything together outside our home.

I said I'll try to stop picking at her, will take her out to dinner once every two weeks, and will go shopping with her at the Artisans' Market. I believe we'll get on a better track.

2010

It does no good to tell Cathy or anyone else how depressed I am. Doing so doesn't make me feel better and can alarm the other person. It can cause awkwardness with friends that may never go away. Better to retreat within myself and bide my time until relief comes.

* * *

An accurate indicator of good mental health is that I listen to music often. I haven't put on a CD for weeks.

* * *

This despondency isn't permanent – it ebbs and flows. This truth should sustain me when I doubt I can go on much longer.

Inevitably good days follow the excruciating ones. I'm always in transition.

* * *

To some extent, I doubt the legitimacy of my mental illness. If I'd asked my server at Denny's today if I felt suicidal, surely she would have said no, since I smiled and joked through my pain. Decades ago, when we spoke by phone about a prescription refill, Dr. Apostle told me, "You don't sound depressed." Is my facade that effective? Or am I a fraud?

* * *

With all this talk about taking my life, why have I never attempted it? Answer: I have an overwhelming desire to live.

* * *

I feel eccentric having a bed in my office suite. No one must know I spend a night a week here, like it reveals a character flaw. It suggests I'm unstable (which is true but hardly a felony) or have marital problems. I don't want others to gossip because I accept their imagined judgments.

Is there something sick about this thinking? Yes. It implies I don't acknowledge my struggles as genuine.

* * *

I feel helpless because there's no cure for this depression. It's not a matter of if I'll do away with myself but when. My goal

is to postpone it as long as possible. For now, self-reproach
prevents me from abandoning my family.

* * *

Another session with my new therapist. I told her my choices
are (1) feeling despondent because of confinement and responsibility at our loving home and (2) if I bolt back to Oregon,
feeling dejected out of loneliness and guilt from squandering
our finances. My options lie with either intimacy or freedom,
each at a huge cost.

* * *

My therapist opens my wounds a little deeper then picks at the
scabs.

* * *

What a wonderful Father's Day! On her card, Jenny wrote,
"I'm glad to have had you as a father these 18 years and continue to!" Cathy wrote, "My wish this year, sweetheart, is that
you and Jenny realize how lucky you both are."

Chapter 5
2011-2019

2011

I've conditioned myself to expect life will sail smoothly and that delays, inconveniences, and breakdowns won't happen. I set myself up to feel depressed when glitches occur.

* * *

Today this sinkhole comes from everything going wrong. I magnify small issues, such as a man smoking on the restaurant patio at lunch. And I deeply regret shortcomings, like spending so little time with Jenny while she was young. I feel like such a failure, that I'm no good to anyone. Suicide would allow me to escape.

Did I feel this way as a child living alone with Mother? That death would be the only way out?

* * *

Action plan: After a stressful day, before going home, inoculate myself with positive thoughts. Affirm *My spirits will not sink tonight. I will not fall apart. I will not lose control.*

* * *

I continue to suffer from PTSD, which got worse after Jenny's birth, and, although she's nineteen, my symptoms still echo back to childhood. My subconscious mind persists in confusing Cathy with Mother, shouldering me with more responsibility than I can bear. I feel like a former combat soldier who now works in a munitions testing facility.

* * *

I asked Cathy to try to empathize with me when I feel despondent. To ask herself how she'd like me to treat her if she felt hopeless, like the time she took prednisone. If she were that down, what would she want from me?

* * *

At 5:20 this morning, Cathy awoke with a pounding heart and considered asking me to take her to the emergency room. We talked and figured stress probably brought it on.

This incident has shaken me. If I'd killed myself like I planned last month, who would have been here for her? With Jenny off to college? No one.

* * *

I have absolutely no confidence in finding a medication or supplement that would restore my mental health. If I tried another promising one, surely my body wouldn't tolerate it and the trial would crush me, requiring Norpramin. That would raise my stress level further. Knowing I don't have to search further brings some relief.

* * *

Since my request for empathy a few weeks ago, Cathy is always cheerful, always glad to hear from me when I phone, always happy to see me when I get home. I'm so grateful for her support.

* * *

It's Thanksgiving and tonight I felt like the ghost of someone who died incomplete. I wanted everyone to understand me and pay attention to my pain and help me find peace. But I didn't ask.

2012

I have no one to tell about these suicidal thoughts. Cathy doesn't know how to handle them, or is it my reluctance to make her sad? If I talked to my therapist, he'd say he has a legal mandate to notify authorities if I plan to harm myself, so that effectively shuts off communication. I'm stuck dealing with this situation on my own. I wish for a friend who would listen nonjudgmentally, then offer encouragement.

It did not occur to me in 2012 to phone a free, confidential depression or suicide prevention hotline. These are available in English and other languages 24/7. I could have Googled "depression hotline" or "suicide hotline."

* * *

When I picked up my computer this morning, I flirted with a woman customer. I wanted her to smile at me, like me, maybe ask for my phone number. Where does this come from? Childhood. I'm addicted to women's attention because Mother gave me so little.

* * *

Walking my familiar route to lunch this morning, I chatted
with two acquaintances. They were so glad to see me and
showered the short story I wrote with compliments. One said,
"We don't know anything about you," implying, I thought,
they'd like to learn more. I felt touched, and confessed I struggle with depression and that writing helps. One said, "Thanks
for sharing." My candor pleases me and I don't think I revealed too much.

                              * * *

Hoping to alleviate stress, I experimented with an herbal remedy that made me despondent. I must accept this situation and
bear the letdown. I'm lucky to have Norpramin, which should
restore my good mood within a day or two. Many others
would envy me.

                              2013

On New Year's Day, our septic tank backed up and flooded the
basement. I handled necessary tasks: shut off the water pump,
arranged for a plumber to repair the ruptured pipe, and filed
an insurance claim. My stress level was moderate. But now
I'm struggling to deal with the enormous disruption; restoration will go on at least a month. Dark water ruined some of
our possessions. No one would blame me if I took my life.

                              * * *

The flood restoration is complete. Although we had insurance,
repairs cost $5,000. In perspective, it could have been much
worse.

* * *

Cathy and Jenny returned from their summer vacation yesterday, and the shock from renewed confinement and heightened
responsibility daunts me. I'm still reacting to stressors as a
child would, as Jenny would have while she was growing up if
Mother had been her sole parent.

Would hypnosis allow me to visualize myself as an adult? The
book I bought says it reprograms the brain and disarms the
conscious mind long enough to communicate directly with the
subconscious. Suggestibility is greatly heightened. I'm going
to give it a try.

* * *

I found a hypnotist and had my appointment this afternoon.
He put me in a trance and did his best to help me. But his efforts failed to make a dent in my ability to forgive Mother and I
still feel like a child. I see no reason to go back. How disappointing this didn't work out.

* * *

After enduring horrible moods due to a tetracycline injection to
treat a gum infection, I will restart Norpramin tonight. How
frustrating I couldn't handle this situation without intervention, but this does not mean I'm a failure. That word would
apply if I ignored reality and refused to take the drug.

* * *

Several times this fall when I felt disheartened, my writing sustained me. I've written several short stories and believe the *Mining History Journal* will publish my biography of mapmaker Emil Fischer.

2014

I survived another Christmas and another basement flood. Every day I grieve my loss of capacity to handle stress. A fine line separates grief from self-pity.

* * *

Walking to lunch today, I picked up a steel dinner knife some-one had discarded next to the street. It symbolizes cutting the cord that binds me to mental illness.

* * *

Feeling lost, today I had a two-hour appointment with another naturopath who prescribed a homeopathic remedy. The cure she selected for Cathy last month made her stomach worse, but she expressed 95% confidence nux vomica is the one that will overcome my depression and stress. I'm anxious but will start it tomorrow. She said I should feel some relief within two weeks.

* * *

After taking it just three days, I'm giving up on nux vomica because it's made me even more stressed-out. What a waste of hope and money.

* * *

Today my contentious office landlord gave me notice. I have to leave by June 15 because he needs the space to expand his business. I'm trying not to panic – that's six weeks away. But my world is falling apart. I feel like a child again: powerless, doomed.

* * *

Today I signed a lease for a new office suite that's somewhat more expensive but quieter and much more spacious than my previous one. Its oversized windows face a peaceful duck pond. My neighbors, all therapists, are congenial. I won't miss the tenseness and negativity I've endured the last year. Everything is working out; I should have trusted it would.

* * *

I took Tylenol for knee pain and – surprise! It brought me out of despondency following the drive to Bellingham for Jenny's graduation [from Western Washington]. Studies showed, in rats, the painkiller passed through the blood-brain barrier to increase both serotonin and norepinephrine levels.[10] It seems an effective substitute for Norpramin that might prove easier to manage.

* * *

---

[10] See https://www.ncbi.nlm.nih.gov/pubmed/11770008,
   https://www.ncbi.nlm.nih.gov/pmc/articles/PMC4912877/.

I've discovered that vigorously massaging my stiff neck causes my moods to sink. Evidently, like chiropractic adjustment and acupuncture, it releases toxins into the system, and drinking several glasses of water afterward doesn't prevent dejection. I have to choose between mental and physical discomfort.

* * *

The bubble burst. After taking Tylenol off and on for three months, last night I felt deeply depressed, abandoned it, and restarted Norpramin. I'm guessing it supplied too much serotonin, which my body does not seem to need, and threw my brain chemistry out of balance.

* * *

The past two nights, again I got extremely upset and stressed-out when things went wrong at home, provoking suicidal thoughts. If only I could tolerate a fast-acting tranquilizer like Valium, which I tried in 1995. It failed to calm me down and caused horrible nightmares when I withdrew. How come it works for other people and not me? But how fortunate my body has the ability to right itself without intervention if I exercise willpower, remove myself from stressors, and wait.

2015

Last night I felt inconsolable and today Cathy brought me tulips.

* * *

After taking Norpramin 27 consecutive days, I recognize addiction. After each dose increase, my body craves more and keeps my moods low. I no longer need it so will begin tapering off tonight. But I have to remain patient. From previous experience, I know when I withdraw too quickly, my body can't adapt and I have to restart the drug soon after.

* * *

My physician prescribed Ludiomil, an antidepressant I tried in 1981. I took it two days ago; it did not improve my mood, plus it made me tired, sleepy, stressed-out, spacey, and numb. Back to Norpramin.

Although its side effects are daunting, Norpramin clears up my misery within hours and has never let me down. It boosts mainly norepinephrine. If my level is low, I feel depressed, but if it's high from too much of the drug, I'm stressed-out and anxious. Now and then I feel one or the other at different times during the same day, occasionally at the same time.

* * *

I just listened to the Cowsills' song "I Need a Friend" and my eyes teared up. In Corvallis 36 years ago, I had a dozen close friends, and now, Cathy is practically my only one. But I dare not get involved in any new person's life. For five months, more days than not, melancholy thoughts have dogged me. Although I do ask other people how they are, I lack the wherewithal to go beyond that. I stay aloof but not by choice.

* * *

I'm so frustrated I couldn't tolerate the probiotic. My Internet search found it contained the strains most likely to relieve depression. It certainly made me more relaxed and less stressed-out, but caused despondency and shortness of breath. Damn!

* * *

One of the most compelling reasons to revisit Corvallis is that it gives the opportunity to grieve what I've lost. Especially driving there and back, listening to music popular in 1975-1979, I weep, mourning the loss of the relative freedom from stress and depression I experienced then. I must return soon.

* * *

When low spirits envelop me, sometimes I think cruel, violent thoughts that shock and shame me. I imagine harming our cat or Cathy. The author of an article in the October issue of *Psychology Today* says 91% of men have murderous thoughts, often brought on by stress. So I will accept rather than try to suppress them, and refuse to act on them or judge myself.

* * *

Eating a sweet roll with added calcium citrate made me depressed. Instead of taking Norpramin and enduring its side effects, this time I tried Wellbutrin, an antidepressant that raises dopamine and norepinephrine. The drug lifted my mood within a few hours, but the following day, despondency returned and I had to go back to my standby med. I'm disillusioned – Wellbutrin seemed so promising.

2016

I'm a private person but long for others to know me completely
and love me. This contradiction causes anxiety and I don't
know how to resolve it.

* * *

I've been off Norpramin 69 days and it seems like I stopped it
just last week. Day to day, my moods fluctuate between depression and stress with no apparent cause. But with each rip-
ple, my body may grasp a fraction more how to cope on its
own. Each blip may represent a point on its learning curve. I
must be steadfast.

* * *

I'm jealous of the intimacy Cathy shares with Jenny, how they
kid around with each other. If my moods stabilize, surely
Jenny and I will become closer.

* * *

This week I watched my *Woodstock* videos three times, often
through tears. Although in 1969 I didn't even realize it was
going on, now I'm so sad I didn't attend. The kids were unin-
hibited and had such fun. I envy them. Besides, the festival
symbolized an attribute sorely missing from my current life:
connection. I'm going to start asking a friend to join me for
lunch now and then.

* * *

I criticize others relentlessly and believe it's because I fail to live up to my own personal standards. For example, today I put myself down for not remembering someone's name and for missing the trashcan with a dirty Kleenex. If I lightened up on myself, surely I'd feel more accepting of others' mistakes and transgressions.

2017

Last night I felt so depressed after eating lasagna made with whey, a partial protein, I drafted a suicide note. My morose mood really brought Cathy down. This morning she told me her heart was pounding and stomach, churning. And now *my* blood pressure is 187/86, the highest ever. Surely my brain would NOT tolerate drugs to lower it. I risk death by killing myself if I medicate and by stroke or heart attack if I don't.

* * *

Today I had my fourth session with my new therapist, this time again using the eye movement desensitization and reprocessing (EMDR) technique. In contrast to my 2003 experience, it proved helpful. I focused on a mental image of Mother towering over me, shaking her finger and yelling, "You can't do anything right!" Since then, each day when an angry trigger comes up, I affirm, "Mother, I forgive you. You did the best you could." This act brings a few moments of peace.

* * *

At this week's session, EMDR evoked my worst nightmare: because I'd disobeyed and disappointed her so many times, Mother left me at home alone and did not return. I ate all the food in the kitchen, then lay on my bed in the dark, famished, waiting for God to take me. My religion taught me I'd rise to Heaven. I'd become a girl, what Mother had always wanted. Everyone would hug me and play with me and I'd never go hungry again. I just had to be patient. Since that appointment, I seem less angry.

* * *

On my psychiatrist's advice, once more I tried Effexor, an antidepressant I took without success in 2002 and 2004. Within eight hours, it cleared up the depression, but that evening my mood plummeted. I doubled the dose and experimented with different amounts for seven days, yet ended up crying uncontrollably like before. Back to Norpramin.

* * *

Yesterday evening I attended a NAMI [National Alliance on Mental Illness] reading at Fact & Fiction and felt out of place as others told about their struggles with depression. I belong to the local chapter but do not want to admit I'm one of them.

* * *

This month I've felt certain I needed Norpramin regularly. Others take their antidepressants every day; why should I be different? I maintained a small dose, only 2.5 mg, a challenge to split because the 10 mg tablets are tiny. But again I could not endure the same stress and shortness of breath that occurred on higher doses. Next, hoping my body would adapt, I took it in the morning instead of the evening, then medicated every other day. Both endeavors failed.

* * *

I came up with a radical procedure my physician questioned: dissolve a 10 mg Norpramin tablet in 100 ml water with a few drops of lime juice as a preservative. I filled a syringe (without needle) with precisely 1 mg of the drug, my lowest dose ever, and swallowed it. But my body still would not tolerate the side effects. Then I took .5 and, a few days later, just .1 mg with the same outcome. How could my body be that sensitive?

* * *

This time my psychiatrist prescribed Cymbalta, indicated for both depression and generalized anxiety disorder. It seemed so promising but deepened my despondency. So I crawled back to Norpramin.

* * *

I wrote a depression survival guide,[11] consisting of 36 suggestions, and mailed it electronically to 745 NAMI chapters. The directors or other personnel at 127 replied they found the article beneficial and many have posted it on their websites. I'm grateful my mental illness gives me this opportunity to serve.

2018

Today I attended the local NAMI chapter annual meeting and realize I have an obligation to help eliminate the stigma attached to mental illness. When I'm feeling despondent and someone asks in a sincere way how I am, I have a duty to tell

---

[11] See Appendix II.

the truth. It's no different from saying I have a bad cold. By speaking candidly, I give others permission to acknowledge their own mental illness, talk about it, and seek help. I must break the silence instead of treating my depression like a shameful character flaw.

* * *

I'd been off Norpramin ten days and felt deeply depressed. This time, instead of taking it alone, I combined it with a low dose of Wellbutrin, hoping to get the ratio right. Although my mood lifted for a while, a day later it collapsed. So I continued Norpramin alone and, as always, it worked its magic. Today I feel cheerful and will begin tapering off. This was another unsuccessful attempt to find a medication regimen with less daunting side effects but I have to keep striving.

* * *

Last night I took just .005 mg of Norpramin. Today I'm fine mentally but still short of breath and will go off it tonight. Since I withdrew very slowly this time, my body may learn to control my moods on its own so I can quit the drug for good.

* * *

After being off Norpramin only five days, I had to restart it again. I don't get it. A microdose of .005 mg, practically nothing, causes debilitating stress and breathing difficulty, yet I cannot manage to stay off the medication. Logic tells me I need to take it every day. Why can't I figure this out?

* * *

The belief I am unlovable defies reason. I'm honest, kind, caring, compassionate, patient, and generous. But sound judgment isn't enough. My erroneous belief resides in a child's locked box.

* * *

Two days ago I reduced Norpramin to .001 mg, so small it's almost impossible to measure, and stopped dosing, certain I could stay off it. But today I'm depressed and clearly need it again. I have the choice between feeling dejected with no intervention and exhausted from the tiniest amount. I'm angry I can't solve this riddle.

* * *

Tonight I told my server-friend at the Mustard Seed about my medication dilemma. She hugged me and said I'm strong and smart. Maybe she's right. I'll keep trying.

* * *

Hopes high, I tried Vivactil, an antidepressant in the same class[12] as Norpramin with a longer half-life. But after three days, I couldn't stand the exhaustion, shortness of breath, nightmares, and insomnia. So I stopped it and went back to Norpramin.

* * *

---

[12] Tricyclic antidepressant (TCA).

I had an appointment with a new board-certified psychiatrist, and what a letdown. He believes the only neurotransmitter that improves mood is serotonin and wanted to write me a script for Zoloft, which I tried in 1993 without results. It, like the other two SSRIs,[13] failed to lift my depression. He will not renew my prescription for Norpramin. I feel deeply discouraged.

* * *

A knowledgeable and caring psychiatric nurse, in the same group as the psychiatrist I saw last month, agreed to restore my Norpramin prescription but thought I might respond favorably to Ritalin. It raises dopamine and norepinephrine levels. But even a low dose behaved just like Norpramin: it fixed the depression and caused the same side effects. The tablets don't dissolve in water so I can't take microdoses. I made a huge emotional investment in Ritalin but realize Norpramin is the more effective choice.

* * *

My therapist helped me map out a plan for the next time I feel suicidal and believe I may not be able to get through the day. First, I would e-mail my psychiatric nurse, who checks for messages hourly, even on weekends. If she couldn't meet with me or talk by phone, I'd call the Urgent Mental Health Clinic, where she works, hoping another provider could help me. If that didn't work out, I'd drive to the emergency room, which has a psychiatrist available at the hospital. With a strategy in place, I feel some comfort.

---

[13] Selective serotonin reuptake inhibitors.

2019

My psychiatric nurse wrote me a prescription for Nuvigil, a medication that promotes wakefulness and can help with treatment-resistant depression. It raises the same neurotransmitters as Ritalin but, I thought, might not tire me as much. For three days it controlled my despondency but, like Ritalin and Norpramin, exhausted me. And it caused a severe rash that covers half my body.

* * *

I twisted my knee March 9 walking across snow to lunch, causing a huge effusion[14] that would not resolve. I relented and for several days took Mobic, a new (to me) nonsteroidal anti-inflammatory drug, recognizing it might affect me mentally. It reduced the swelling but, as I feared, made me severely depressed. Norpramin eventually restored my mood but flared the Nuvigil rash, then I had to face another excruciating withdrawal. In hindsight, after my injury, I should have taken aspirin, which I knew from experience would have made me feel dejected but would not have required as high a dose of the antidepressant.

* * *

Writing *Quest Without a Compass* sustains me. When I think about taking my life, I tell myself I must finish this book.

* * *

---

[14] An escape of fluid into a body cavity.

A few days ago, I felt livid after the live-in manager at a mental-health rehabilitation home on my route to lunch berated me for walking in unannounced and requesting the residents not sit by the sidewalk and smoke cigarettes. When I left, he stalked me for a block. I lost control and called him a bastard. Then I felt hurt, sad, and ashamed.

After reflecting on the situation, I admitted to myself my problem and bought *Anger Management for Dummies*. I started reading it yesterday and already feel more peaceful. Priority number one: forgive the manager and, two, myself. I will also drop my sense of entitlement and stop expecting others to always treat me kindly and fairly.

* * *

I'm in Denver for Jenny's graduation with her masters in City Planning. I feel antisocial and so different from everyone else but am trying not to infect their moods. I felt caged on the plane getting here, trapped between Cathy on one side and an obnoxious passenger who invaded my space on the other. Since I abandoned my routines, they cannot prop me up. Resolved: I will never fly again except in case of emergency.

* * *

Yesterday I phoned the Mayo Clinic in Minnesota and made an appointment to address treatment-resistant depression. But today I'm having second thoughts. I'd have to endure two plane changes each way (unthinkable) and enormous expense, plus spend five to seven business days away from my routines. Cathy offered to go with me, but what would I do with my free time between sessions in a frightening, unfamiliar city? I don't think I could stand the stress, besides the likely disappointment the doctors' prescriptions would leave me no better off.

* * *

A friend suggested checking out transcranial magnetic stimulation[15] for healing depression. This benign procedure involves taking no medication that could make my disorder worse. But we don't have a TMS provider in Missoula. I interpret this as a sign it wouldn't help.

* * *

I decided not to travel to the Mayo Clinic. Instead, I made an appointment for July 3 with a board-certified psychiatrist in Helena, since I've exhausted the resources in Missoula. I must explore every possible avenue to improve my quality of life.

* * *

The Helena psychiatrist made five suggestions to alleviate my despondency but none seems promising: a thyroid hormone (my recent test showed normal function); lithium (in 2005 it caused both stress and depression and required Norpramin); a small SSRI dose (the three I've tried did not help); niacin (in 1989 it did not help); and an antipsychotic, Abilify (which reportedly causes anxiety). I'm afraid all these would aggravate

---

[15] Transcranial magnetic stimulation is a noninvasive procedure that delivers repetitive magnetic pulses to the brain to stimulate nerve cells. TMS is typically used for treatment-resistant depression. See https://www.mayoclinic.org/tests-procedures/transcranial-magnetic-stimulation/about/pac-20384625.

my condition. I doubt I can improve on Norpramin. This was a misspent four-hour trip that dashed my expectations.

* * *

I read an article in *Psychology Today* about ketamine[16] intravenous infusions and considered them. But the medication targets, unlike me, those who feel despondent all the time. Also, therapy might require multiple treatments that cost $500 each over a number of weeks with no Medicare coverage, since the FDA has not approved it for depression. I cannot justify the expense for a remedy of questionable benefit.

* * *

After being off Norpramin just three days, I needed it again and took .01 mg August 21, .005 mg the 22nd, and .002 mg the 23rd. I'm hoping that by withdrawing more slowly than ever before, I can stay off it.

* * *

Yesterday I discovered a new TMS provider in Missoula but will not rush to make an appointment. Medicare does cover the cost but I might not need it, since I haven't felt depressed for a while. Why commit to treatments five times a week for

---

[16] Ketamine is a prescription anesthetic that holds promise for treating major depression and, because of its rapid action, preventing suicide. Ketamine can also be effective for treating depression combined with anxiety. See https://www.health.harvard.edu/blog/ketamine-for-major-depression-new-tool-new-questions-2019052216673.

four to six weeks? Besides, I have reservations about the ad-
ministering physician, whom I've seen before.

* * *

Although not depressed, yesterday I took 37.5 mg of Zoloft and
another 25 mg today. An Internet article[17] suggested it might
relieve compulsive scratching of the itch that covers much of
my body, which eczema caused. I took the SSRI in 1993; it
made me more easy-going but I couldn't stand the side effects.

Zoloft didn't reduce the itch but it hasn't made my mood
worse, either. Side effects include slurred speech, foggy
thinking, and shortness of breath, plus it's made my eyes ultra-
sensitive to light. So much for that experiment.

* * *

I've been off Norpramin 57 days and have not felt dejected
during all that time, although I've taken several medications
that lowered my mood in the recent past: ibuprofen, Tylenol,
Benadryl, melatonin, and hydrocodone. Apparently the Zoloft
I took in early November reset my brain and acted like a vac-
cine to head off depression. It's certainly more effective than
Norpramin, so this is the antidepressant I'll reach for the next
time I need one. But I'll take a much smaller dose and I'll take
it only once.

---

[17] https://www.ncbi.nlm.nih.gov/pmc/articles/PMC5522672/

Afterword

My roller-coaster odyssey with depression has spanned 49 years. Despite wishing to state otherwise, I have not found a lasting solution and cannot wrap up my story with a bow. However, I believe I have transcended my illness in the sense of coming to terms with it and rising above it. Although coming upon a cure seems unlikely, I have reached a comfort level that allows me to tolerate depression, live with it, and function acceptably much of the time, interspersed with periods of contentment, happiness, and even joy.

Ten themes appeared in the voluminous journals that formed the basis of my quest:

- I frequently pondered whether my despondency related to endogenous major depression (caused by a chemical brain imbalance) or the stress-induced type (associated with daily events). Over the years, this debate within myself consumed dozens of pages. Eventually I understood I suffered from each at different times.

- Often I felt convinced I could obey my interior will, control my moods, and bring an end to my melancholy without medication. Other times I felt equally certain pharmaceuticals and supplements constituted my only hope. Each philosophy prevailed during specific intervals.

- I recognized that my mother's abuse when I was a child continued to thwart me as an adult, particularly with respect to responsibility and confinement. Many times I attempted to avoid situations that involved either issue. When that was impossible, I often failed to suppress my negative reactions to the issues' triggers.

- As an adult, to compensate for childhood helplessness, I felt a strong desire to control my environment and make my own choices.

- I endeavored to balance honoring my strong need for the solitude I lacked as a child with setting limits on time alone.

- I continually wavered between seeking the intimacy I'd craved as a child and pushing it away out of fears of rejection and the burdens closeness entails.

- I grappled with the advent of parenthood, then with coping with the lifestyle changes it mandated. Frequently I was able to embrace the satisfaction and delight fatherhood presented.

- For many years, I wrestled with the importance of work as a contributor to self-esteem and daily structure versus the constraints it placed on my free time.

- I felt guilty for what I saw as my shortcomings: abandoning the children from my first marriage when they were young; not giving enough of myself to those I love; not measuring up to rigid standards I'd established for my conduct; not working for months, by choice; not asserting my needs to family and friends; and unfaithfulness to my second wife. But I did often come to realize I was doing my best.

- I affirmed the need to proclaim personal accountability for my actions, for my rehabilitation, and for improving my self-regard. I could not excuse regrettable behavior because of feeling depressed, or blame ongoing despondency on God or other people's acts.

Almost daily I confront emotionally difficult situations that spring up using strategies that evolved during my accumulation of experience. These tactics have made survival attainable, and challenging days easier to bear. I offer the reader my approach.

Although I contemplated suicide many times, and developed concrete plans once or twice, I never gave up. Rather than take the emergency exit, I searched relentlessly for remedies and coping mechanisms. Although often feeling worn down and deeply discouraged, I persisted in hoping better times might come.

Shortly after the onset of my mental illness, I acknowledged it and sought help, figuring I wasn't going to recover on my own. Over the decades, many therapists and psychiatrists, most of them competent and caring, have lent their expertise, and I usually embraced their recommendations and heeded their advice. At the same time, I declined to surrender my quest for recovery to them and instead played an active role myself. Thus far I have experimented with 36 psychiatric medications[18] as well as over two dozen supplements, including vitamins, minerals, amino acids, herbal and homeopathic products, hormones, stomach enzymes, and probiotics. I kept meticulous notes on each, recording dates and strengths, and analyzed the results to determine which helped and which worsened my condition. I also tried acupuncture and hypnosis.

I continue to ask my loved ones for support, providing them the fulfilling opportunity to help, and they give it without reservation. I indulge my cravings for protein and chocolate, both of which are sources of amino acids and, in the case of chocolate, many other mental nutrients. I pray, exercise, and

---

[18] See Appendix I.

meditate. During the midst of a depressive episode, I usually
stay busy, minimizing idle hours when negative thoughts
might come up. I structure my time and stick to routines,
which furnish mileposts to carry me through the day.

I continue to journal, often daily, exploring thoughts and
feelings to discover direction and find validation. I employ introspection and converse with myself through writing. I remind myself this hopelessness, endless as it seems, is temporary and I will overcome it. Rereading the entries months or
years later, I recall previous hard times I weathered and recognize the healing accomplished. My wisdom, resilience, and
strength often surprise me.

As a consequence of adopting these strategies, I have ac-
quired an imperfect compass to navigate the depression labyrinth.

During the course of my journey, two paramount truths
emerged. The first is that the intensity of my mental illness is
not constant. Rough patches, even excruciating ones, prove
short-lived and abate long enough for me to breathe and gain
perspective.

The second is that living is important, for each year I accomplish much good that serves others. If I'd taken my life
along the way, I would have denied those I love, acquaintances
I care for, and, through my writing, strangers I'll never meet,
these gifts: empathy, support, and encouragement.

Appendix I
Psychiatric Medications the Author Has Taken

Brand Name	Generic Name
Anafranil	clomipramine
Ascendin	amoxapine
Ativan	lorazepam
BuSpar	buspirone
Cymbalta	duloxetine
Depakote	valporic acid
Desyrel	trazodone
Effexor	venlafaxine
Eldepryl	selegiline
Eskalith	lithium
Hydergene	ergoloid mesylates
Klonopin	clonazepam
Lexapro	escitalopram
Ludiomil	maprotiline
Manerix	moclobemide
Mellaril	thioridazine
Merital	nomifensine
Minipress	prazosin
Mirapex	pramipexole
Navane	thiothixene
Neurontin	gabapentin
Norpramin	desipramine
Nuvigil	armodafinil
Pamelor	nortriptyline
Prozac	fluoxetine
Remeron	mirtazapine
Risperdal	risperidone
Ritalin	methylphenidate
Serzone	nefazodone
Sinequan	doxepin

Tofranil	imipramine
Valium	diazepam
Vivactil	protriptyline
Wellbutrin	bupropion
Xanax	alprazolam
Zoloft	sertraline

Appendix II
Depression Survival Guide

Although I am not a healthcare professional, I've seen depression from the inside. My expertise is rooted in the trials and errors of personal experience. Each person is different, so not all these suggestions will work for you, just as they haven't all worked for me. My hope is that through this guide, you'll gain insight into at least one new strategy that helps assuage your depression. The following list is not exhaustive – therapies I didn't mention might help you and if they do, by all means stick to them.

1. Recognize that depression is not a sign of weakness. Unfortunately, many people don't understand this. A stigma can discourage us from getting help, but know you are not alone. Millions, including celebrities as well as everyday people, have talked about their struggles with depression, received help, and are in recovery.

2. Get help from a professional. Don't figure you'll get better on your own. Make an appointment with a healthcare provider, whether it's your family physician, a licensed mental health professional, or a psychiatrist. Choose one you feel comfortable with. If you can't afford the cost for a private visit, call your local county health services department or mental health center for assistance. Or check out the SAMHSA Behavioral Health Treatment Locator at www.findtreatment.samhsa.gov.

3. Don't suffer in silence. Call up a warmline, which is a free, peer-run listening line staffed by people in recovery themselves. Check out www.warmline.org. Or call a

hotline to speak confidentially and anonymously with a
trained support staff member or volunteer. Google "depression hotline" to find Internet chat and toll-free phone
options. Your local mental health center might also provide recommendations.

4. Get personal support. Confide in those you trust,
   whether it's your spouse or partner, a relative, or a close
   friend, as well as your healthcare providers. You can also
   join a support group, either a face-to-face one in your
   community or online. At the same time, be selective in
   how much you disclose about your illness when a casual
   friend or acquaintance asks how you are.

5. Change doctors or therapists from time to time. Each
   healthcare provider possesses his or her own area of expertise and personal experience to draw from, and brings
   a unique slant to your symptoms. If one doesn't seem the
   best fit for you, try another.

6. If you're taking medications but haven't found relief,
   NEVER GIVE UP. You'll find dozens of antidepressants
   on the market, including SSRIs, SNRIs, tricyclics, and
   MAO inhibitors. Even within each family, every drug
   behaves a bit differently in its effect on the brain's neurotransmitters. Also, the FDA approves new antidepressants every year. If your doctor suggests a drug that's
   still on patent, ask if an older, cheaper generic might do
   instead. Fortunately, pharmaceutical companies offer
   patient-assistance programs that lower the cost of pat-
   ented drugs for low-income people. Don't forget to ask
   your doctor for samples.

7. Be patient. Although some treatments, including a few antidepressants, can yield results within a day or two, many take weeks to make a difference. Follow your physician's directions – don't exceed what he or she recommends. Look for gradual improvement rather than significant changes overnight.

8. Don't despair if your body is grappling with a medication's side effects. Your doctor may be able to prescribe a different suitable one with fewer undesirable results. If not, keep in mind you may not have to take the drug long-term – a short trial may suffice. And in the meantime, a more body-friendly drug may come on the market.

9. If you decide to go off an antidepressant, withdraw slowly in consultation with your physician. Allow your brain to adjust to the change so you reduce the risk of a rebound and other distressing effects.

10. Try supplements. A multi-vitamin, multi-mineral, or amino acid blend might provide relief. Consider taking probiotics, SAMe, Omega-3 fatty acids, acetaminophen (Tylenol), 5-HTP, St. John's wort, GABA, or melatonin. If you're taking antidepressants, keep in mind some supplements might interact negatively with them, so check with your doctor and pharmacist.

11. Try acupuncture or acupressure.

12. Let your healthcare provider know immediately if an antidepressant, a supplement, or acupuncture seems to make you feel more depressed. Some therapies may in-

crease detrimental neurotransmitters or dampen helpful
ones for certain individuals.

13. Experiment with only one new drug, supplement, or pro-
     cedure at a time, to isolate your observations and arrive at
     accurate conclusions. With each, strike a balance between
     optimism and realistic expectations. Selecting the best
     therapy is not an exact science and the process often in-
     volves trial and error. Have patience. If the current rem-
     edy doesn't pan out, go on to the next, in consultation
     with your physician.

14. Keep a log. Write down your experience with each drug
     or supplement, both to share with your healthcare pro-
     vider and to track results for future reference. He or she
     may want you to try it again later, at a different dose or in
     concert with another product. Some medications have a
     therapeutic window, that is, the dose must be fairly pre-
     cise. Keep notes on dates, dosage amounts, times of the
     day you take it, side effects, and results.

15. If you feel more depressed after taking a steroid, pain-
     killer, or other medication for a condition other than de-
     pression, make a note of it and try to avoid it in the fu-
     ture.

16. Consider these alternative treatments: transcranial mag-
     netic stimulation (TMS), ketamine infusions, and light-
     box therapy.

17. Eat healthy foods. Visit the Wikipedia website and enter
     "healthy diet" in the search bar.

18. If you crave chocolate, eat more, in moderation. Aim for a product with a high cocoa content (80-99%) and low sugar. Chocolate contains tyrosine, tryptophan, and phenylethylamine, all of which can boost your mood.

19. Watch your alcohol consumption. Alcohol can contribute to depression and cause negative interactions with your antidepressants.

20. Try yoga.

21. Practice meditation. In a quiet place, focus on your breathing and try to let thoughts that come up drift away.

22. Practice mindfulness. Become aware of your surroundings, your body, and your actions, without judgment, to ground you and connect you to the present moment.

23. Seek sunlight. When weather permits, walk in the sun or sit indoors beside a sunny window. On cloudy days, full-spectrum light bulbs might help but they could make you feel worse.

24. Journal. Explore your thoughts and feelings in a private place, on paper or disk. Just writing them down and reviewing or revising them can bring validation and relief. Let out any anger and frustrations instead of bottling them up. Reread past entries to remind yourself you survived previous hard times.

25. Talk to yourself, either silently at any time or aloud in private. Keep your inner dialogue positive. Tell yourself

you are going to get better. Tell yourself this condition is
temporary and you will overcome it.

26. Create a rainy-day fund for times when you hit a rough
    patch. Depression can come in cycles, so prepare your-
    self. Keep a list of activities that make you smile and
    laugh. These might include calling a friend, looking
    through photos from a fun vacation, listening to a playlist
    of your favorite songs, watching a funny cat video, or re-
    reading inspirational quotes.

27. Stay busy. Fill your agenda every day. Consider volun-
    teering to help others, which will likely give you a posi-
    tive feeling from contributing to make the world a better
    place. Take up a new hobby or enroll in an interesting
    class. Keep idle time, when you're apt to dwell on nega-
    tive thoughts, to a minimum.

28. Pursue activities you find fun or relaxing. Paint, garden,
    read, watch movies, or attend concerts and sporting
    events. Spend time doing whatever makes you feel at
    peace.

29. Stick to your daily routines. They provide structure and
    stability, furnishing mileposts to carry you through until
    bedtime.

30. Occasionally break with routine and take a vacation or
    staycation.

31. Exercise. Take long walks, jog, play tennis, or lift
    weights. Join a fitness club. Aerobic exercise burns calo-
    ries and releases endorphins, which can reduce stress and

lift your mood. If you haven't exercised in a while or have never really gotten into it, set a small goal to start: just 10-15 minutes several times a week. Once you create an exercise routine, sticking to it will become easy.

32. Distance yourself from negative people and situations as much as you can. Negativity breeds more negativity, making it hard to stop the cycle. Surround yourself with positive people, ones who make you happy.

33. Pray.

34. Pet your cat or dog. If you don't have one, befriend a neighbor's or visit an animal shelter.

35. Listen to uplifting music, such as the first movement of Schubert's *Symphony No. Nine.*

36. Be compassionate with yourself. Forgive yourself for your blunders and for angry remarks you may have made. Realize you're doing the best you can. But don't get complacent – resolve to do better in the future.

Appendix III
Chess in the Labyrinth

The King represents the being over whom the Battle rages. If his enemy captures him, he loses the game. He signifies the deeper self, the divine spark that rejoices to spot blossoms on the cherry tree, hugs a friend who suffered a loss, and paints fresh snow on a mountain at sunrise. Although the most important piece, he is the weakest, capable of taking only a single step at a time through the maze to heal himself; his strength rests in the distribution of powers to his soldiers.

The Queen is the King's chief support person and confidante, commonly his spouse, partner, or best friend. She reflects the King's light and contains unlimited potential to invigorate him. The most powerful and versatile piece, she possesses full freedom of movement in any direction through the labyrinth's passages. The Queen loves her King unconditionally – she pays attention to what he says, persuades him he will succeed, makes allowances, and forgives him. She buys him a mum, phones to ask how he's feeling, and picks up his prescription at the pharmacy. She offers the music of her soul to soothe and comfort him.

The Bishops personify the King's therapist, physician, and minister, rabbi, or priest. Their mission is to serve him with resources they embrace by virtue of specialized training. These pieces empathize with the King, give counsel, raise hope, and prescribe medication. They encourage him to take long walks, stick to his routines, fill his agenda every day to stay busy, and eat healthy food. The Bishops protect him from dark thoughts and impulses, recalling which specific therapies made their other clients, patients, and churchgoers whole. The spiritual leaders act as pathways to God, the ultimate caregiver, directly accessible 24/7, if the King chooses.

The Knights embody pharmaceuticals and supplements a Bishop selects that race to the King's brain to achieve balance by altering chemicals that affect mood. They are the only pieces on the board capable of leaping over the others, those of both the King and his opponent. They can overcome obstacles that appear insurmountable. Sometimes proceeding by trial and error, a Bishop may change course and assign a different Knight. Although physicians competently utilize the tools available to them, they may step aside to allow another Bishop to assume command and restore the King's health.

The Rooks symbolize the watchers, the observers of both the King's exterior (the events that occur every day) and his interior thoughts. Their castle walls, composed of reason and logic, safeguard the King, Queen, and Bishops. In concert with his Rooks, the King employs introspection, journaling to explore thoughts and feelings, positive self-talk, meditation, and willpower. As he applies these strategies, his brain processes information accurately, decides what's relevant, sets goals, makes commitments for his highest good, and assesses progress. These pieces remind him this situation is temporary and implore the King to exercise patience while marching down the path toward recovery.

The Pawns comprise the fighters on the front line, the ordinary men and women who move one step at a time, always forward, never backward, utilizing both the head and the heart, in a quest to mend their King. They represent his friends, coworkers, neighbors, and restaurant servers, who listen, advise, or simply smile. A Pawn can become his Queen. Some may remain ignorant of the King's struggles but, without trying, lend energy and unspoken compassion. If he elects to trust and confide in them, they may affirm and enhearten. These pieces include strangers from Internet chat groups, and pets who intuitively comprehend and sympathize without expectation. They form a network that underlies the interventions of the King's other team members and bolsters their probability of success.

The Battle plays out on cloudy days, with a distant shaft of sunlight, over weeks, months, or years. The stakes are high. Although the King's soldiers work together, he doesn't require them all – a single Bishop, Knight, Rook, or Pawn, or his Queen, could suffice to win. He faces a relentless adversary; however, with perseverance and his allies' aid, he will prevail.

Made in the USA
Middletown, DE
12 April 2021

37492090R00089